STROKE: Brain-Assault

STROKE:
Brain-Assault

*Suggestions, Encouragement, and Exercises
to Help You or Your Loved One
Overcome the Effects
of a Stroke*

Madelina A. DePaz

Symposium

Published by Symposium Publishing
an imprint of Blue Dolphin Publishing, Inc.

For inquiries or orders, address
Blue Dolphin Publishing, Inc.
P.O. Box 8, Nevada City, CA 95959
1-800-643-0765
www.bluedolphinpublishing.com

ISBN: 1-57733-074-9

Library of Congress Cataloging-in-Publication Data

DePaz, Madelina A., 1940–
    Stroke : brain-assault : suggestions, encouragement and
    exercises to help you or your loved one overcome the effects of
    a stroke / Madelina A. DePaz
        p. cm.
    Includes bibliographical references.
    ISBN 1-57733-074-9
    1. DePaz, Madelina A., 1940—Health. 2. Cerebrovascular
    disease—Patients—United States—Biography. I. Title.

RC388.5 .D45 2000
616.8'1—dc21
[B]
                                                      00-050506

Book Illustrations by Jonathan N. DePaz
Cover Photo by Cathy Maudlin
First edition, August, 2002

Printed in the United States of America

10   9   8   7   6   5   4   3   2   1

To the men in my life:
Jonathan Nowell, Tatay, Gelong,
Orinako, and to my Savior—
before, today, and forever.

Some of life's promises don't come true—
but mornings still come—
and sparrows, like hopes, ...
still sing in the trees.

—Flavia

TABLE OF CONTENTS

PROLOGUE

I AM COMPELLED TO WRITE THIS BOOK, to relate my experience to thousands of people in the United States who are affected by stroke, the number one cause of major long-term disability and the third leading cause of death by disease. Every sixty (60) seconds someone suffers a stroke and every three and a half (3-1/2) minutes someone dies from stroke. Each year, stroke hits six-hundred thousand (600,000) Americans, killing about one-hundred sixty thousand (160,000) of its victims and over one million survivors become permanently disabled. Stroke hits anyone—young or old.

Known as cerebrovascular accident (CVA), it occurred very sudden, in my case. There was no warning sign. It began with numbness and paralysis and in less than an hour, I was comatose. Stroke is not debilitating. But I believe that a victim has to fight. It is true that brain cells die and are not replaced by new nerve cells or neurons. However, the brain has the capacity to compensate the permanently damage fragments. The connected tissue can adjust some and the lost functions may be recovered through therapy and hard work.

The stroke-assault is devastating. The fact that it happened, I confronted it and refused to give in. I feel I am in control of my recovery. I mine the abyss of my mental power.

This is my story.

1

FROM THE MIDWEST TO NEW ENGLAND

CHICAGO WAS NAMED AFTER the Indian word *checagou*, meaning, wild onions that grew in the marshland. It is the third largest city in the United States populated by a conglomerate of cultures. Between the eighteenth and nineteenth centuries, an influx of immigrants from the southern and eastern Europe, mainly, from Poland, Italy, Bohemia, Lithuania, Greece, Serbia, Hungary, and Russia came to join the Chicago workforce.

On October 8, 1871, the Great Chicago Fire broke out. It was believed that a cow kicked over a lantern in the O'Leary's barn. The northeasterly wind which fanned the northward wind along the lakeshore, fed the fire and worked havoc virtually in every structure in the city. The fire burned until October 10. About one-hundred thousand (100,000) homes were burned and hundreds of people died.

The City of Chicago is situated along the shore of Lake Michigan. It is very rich in architectural heritage and proud to have fine early modern era architecture. It has world-class shopping, dining, entertaining and has a notable museum of art which highlights various sculptures and historical buildings. The loop area, which is Chicago downtown, was named after the elevated train tracks bounded by Wabash & Van Buren avenues and Wells & Lake streets.

1

The Great Chicago Fire left a conspicuous legacy—sky-scrapers. The energetic city has famous architects. Skidmore, Owings & Merrill built Sears Tower, the tallest building in the world, with one-hundred ten (110) stories and one-thousand four-hundred fifty-four (1454) feet high built in 1974, John Hancock Center in 1970, University of Illinois, Chicago Circle Campus built in 1965-1979, and Inland Steel Building built in 1957; Loebl, Schlossman & Hackl built Water Tower Place in 1976; CF Murphy Associates built Mayor Richard J. Daley Center, previously known as the Chicago Civic Center built in 1967; Ludwig Mies van der Rohe built 860-880 Lakeshore Drive Apartments in 1951, The Federal Government Center in 1963 through 1977 and Illinois Institute of Technology in 1940 through 1958; GD Schipporeit and John C. Heinrich (former students and employees of Ludwig van der Rohe), built Lake Point Tower in 1968; Eliel Saarinen built the Tribune Tower in 1925; Bertrand Goldberg built Marina City in 1962; Dankman Adler and Louis Sullivan built the Carson, Pirie, Scott Building in 1899 and The Auditorium Building in 1889; Shepley, Rutan & Coolidge built The Chicago Public Library Cultural Center in 1897; Frank Lloyd Wright built Frederick C. Robie House in 1906; DH Burnham & Company built Museum of Science and Industry in 1893; Henry Hobson Richardson built the John J. Glessner House in 1886; and other illustrious architects.

In wintry Chicago, it is bleak and biting cold where the populace struggles to walk in the avenue. After a day's work, I walked the Magnificent Mile to view the beauty of the city. I took pleasure in strutting through the trodden snow and felt the fresh, white snowflakes covering me. It gave me a sense of being, in a frozen cloud of another world where peace was a touch of winter.

It was Tuesday midnight, the third of April 1975 when the snowstorm began—a sequel to the Great Snow of 1967. The spring blizzard was the worst snowfall in fifty (50) years. It was an unusual day. At three (3) o'clock in the afternoon, it was announced on TV and radio that all offices and schools were shut down due to a serious snowstorm. I looked out of the window from my office and everything I saw was white—trees and roads. As the wind was dancing, the side roads were covered by tons of snow followed by sleet. The stalled cars were filled with snow to the brim and it got deeper in the snow embankment which paralyzed the city by the prodigiousness of winter.

I mulled over a decision to embark a tough job—to get my car out of the outdoor parking lot. As snow was not waning, I shoveled the pathways of my car as far as I could reach. Then inch by inch, I drove through the street while a violent wind prolonged the intensity of snowstorm. My car crawled on the inner drive of lakeshore. Lakeshore Drive, a very imposing boulevard, is an expressway that turns out to be the largest parking lot ever. I maneuvered my small car, an MG Midget, in such a way that I could move as I planned to scheme the snowy area. My vehicle was one of the few that made it miles away. The driving speed was ten (10) miles per hour and it took me six (6) hours to get home which was, normally, fifteen (15) minutes. I was fortunate to see my gas tank outlived.

Chicago has a great way of handling snowstorms. The city streets, primary and secondary, are plowed regularly twenty-four (24) hours a day. The traffic is normal despite the fact that the snowstorm does not let up. The residents on secondary streets do their share of shoveling the pathways, to maintain the visibility of the sidewalks and levels of the ground surface. This is a city where snow is a part of living. People are dressed warmly to be comfortable with the frigid weather. It is typical to wear a hat, wool scarf, coat, socks and boots to survive a freezing existence. No amount of winter coat fabric can give the warmth that a fur coat can.

In December, the cold winter in the city is synonymous to white Christmas, where the glimmering lights make the holiday spirit alive. Along the Magnificent Mile, the illumination gives a perception that there is no night. The lights on the trees are blooming with glitters as in a world of dreams. It is so beautiful that I can walk the Mile with the wind brushing my face with flurries of white virgin snow. I forget the hours that the night seems so young.

In my experience, there are only two seasons in the Windy City—cold winter and hot summer. Autumn gets lost in the winter and summer absorbs the spring. The temperature in the winter is as low as fifteen (15) to twenty-five (25) degrees Fahrenheit below zero and as high as one-hundred five (105) degrees Fahrenheit in the summer. Life is easier in the summer because the days are long where I can enjoy living outdoors— bicycling along the lakefront. It is a good feeling to communicate with the gentle wind, the sun, and the lake.

One day after work, my friend Wili, called me up to go bicycling via the lakefront. With the wind breezing by and playing with the sun and the clime, we swifted through the bike trail which was populated by various bike athletes. In one of the outlets to a busy street, we decided to go to an ice cream parlor. It was a crowded place—very well-liked by the outdoor people. There was a parking lot for bicycles that inspired me to stay longer than we should in order to have an ice cream sundae. Then, we biked back through the city streets as the last glow of sunset sank in.

The following weekend, we started biking in the morning on the same route along the lakefront. But we did not exit onto one of the outlets to the city streets. The day was radiant with the blue sky hovering around while we biked as far as about seven (7) miles from my place, stopped at Adler Planetarium and relaxed on the greens. That was when I realized that I was as tired as a horse. I did not want to bike back home. But I had no choice. I got home later than Wili did because his house was close to the route we took. I took a shower and dressed-up for a night out. For a short time, I sat on the couch. But I fell asleep until the morning sun woke me up. Wili did not make it either, because he napped while waiting for my call.

The City of Chicago is the center of building construction and architecture where I am able to practice my professional career. However, another branch of engineering attracts me. I was interested in nuclear-powered submarines. By chance, I was able to touch base with a defense contractor based in New England.

In the spring of 1984, I moved to the town of Groton, New London County, the southeastern shore of Connecticut (Quinnehtukqut meaning "beside the long tidal river") at the opening of the Thames River on Long Island Sound. The City of Groton settled as part of New London but incorporated in 1964 as a separate town, named for Groton, England.

Along Interstate 95, New London and Groton are separated by Gold Star Memorial Bridge which is about one-and-a-half-miles crossing the Thames River. Eastward, General Dynamics Corporation has the mastery of the low skyline. A few feet away from the end of the bridge is a sign that says: "Groton—The Submarine Capital of the World."

General Dynamics Electric Boat—A Century of Innovation, 1899 to 1999. It is impressive—one of America's largest corporations, a leading defense contractor and the leading designer and builder of submarines for the United States Navy. Since the beginning of the century (1900), with the advent of submarine technology, it has a continuing submarine leadership commitment. In the early 1950s, it designed and built the world's first nuclear-powered submarine—the *Nautilus*.

The company provides the best design, engineering and construction of nuclear submarines. It involves two advanced submarine construction facilities—Land-Level Submarine Construction Facility at the shipyard in Groton, Connecticut and the Automated Submarine Frame and Cylinder Manufacturing Facility at the plant in Quonset Point, Rhode Island. With these facilities, the company remains at the forefront of submarine technology. It produces the following submarines:

The *Ohio Class (SSBN-726)* (also known as Trident), the largest and most powerful submarines ever built in the free world, is 500 feet long with a displacement of 18,750 tons. She carries twenty-four (24) missile tubes in each sub. SSBN stands for Submersible Ship Ballistic Nuclear.

The *Los Angeles Class (SSN-688)*, the most advanced undersea vessels with a mission of hunting down enemy surface ships and submarines, is quiet, fast, and dangerous. She is 360 feet long with a displacement of 6,900 tons. She carries Tomahawk Land Attack Missiles (TLAM) and has the capability of long-range and precise strikes with conventional warheads. SSN stands for Submersible Ship Nuclear.

The *USS Seawolf (SSN21),* the newest attack sub apropos to the new millennium, is the most advanced and the most heavily armed attack submarine in the world "to meet the Cold War requirements against an aggressive Soviet submarine force." Actually, she is a multi-mission stealth warship totally capable of all special tasks on sea control and power projection. She is 377 feet long with a displacement of 7,500 tons. USS stands for United States Ship.

The *NSSN Virginia (SSN774),* the first U.S. warship designed and engineered entirely by computer, is designed for peacetime, crisis, and wartime needs of the new century. With the existence of NSSN (stands for New Submersible Ship Nuclear), the undersea superiority of the United States against all undersea threats will be maintained.

Submarines fascinate me—the engineering, its design and its intent. Being our nation's asset, she is a stealth—invisible and not easy to detect. As a military deterrent, the submarine has the advantage of utilizing ballistic missiles (travel unpowered in a ballistic trajectory), and cruise missiles (travel in the lower atmosphere).

She is built to perform mainly, on or below the ocean. The design of the sub is based on: its structural strength to resist deep sea pressure; its ability to control the sub while submerged and on the surface; its ability to control the atmospheric pressure and nuclear energy in a closed environment for a long time; its ability to launch weapons underwater; and its ability to operate quietly.

Submarines are the most powerful vessel that can be submerged and cruised underwater. She dives deep, numerous hundreds of feet under the sea. Because of the water crushing pressure, the submarine is designed with a double-layer hull, one hull over the other. The inner hull of the submarine's pressure hull, built from special high-yield steel. The shape of the hull is designed with accuracy to compartmentation and to resist the weight of water pressure that fights the sub.

Because some components are mounted externally to the pressure hull, the outer hull, the skin of the submarine, has to surround the inner hull—the oil tank and the water tank. It is streamlined, smooth and shaped like a killer-whale to control the sub with ease. Years ago, the outer hull was constructed with thin plates but it was difficult to control at high speed.

A submarine has bow (front), stern (rear), propeller (angled-blades), front and rear hydroplanes or rudders (movable panels), for maneuverability to execute the intention. The propeller makes the engine move the sub through the water; and the rudder steers the sub to the left or right direction. Located between the inner and outer hull, are the main ballast tanks (to make great changes in the buoyancy for submerging or surfacing) and variable ballast tanks (to make subtle adjustment of the sub's weight, and to control trim and list). The ballast tanks have two valves on top—for the compressed air to exit and two valves at the bottom—for the seawater to enter.

In order for the sub to dive underwater (negative buoyancy), the valves are opened to let the compressed air to come out, the seawater to come in, and the tanks to be flooded. When the forward hydroplanes are tilted downward and the back hydroplanes upward, the sub is nose-down driving deep underwater. When the forward hydroplanes are tilted upward and the back hydroplanes downward, the sub is nose-up driving to rise to the surface. For the sub to surface (positive buoyancy) while submerged, the top valves of the ballast tanks are closed to trap the compressed air and the bottom valves are opened to push the seawater out.

A submerged submarine has to be kept on even keel and not allowed to roll, by the use of trim tanks—fore, aft, port and starboard. To maintain the level, water is pumped from fore to aft trim tanks. And to keep her from rolling, water is pumped from port to starboard (side to side) trim tanks.

The submarine has a nuclear reactor that produces heat to turn water to steam which makes the turbines rotate the propeller and urge the submarine to move through the water stealthily and undetected. She carries torpedoes and can launch missiles while submerged. She can, also, lay mines underwater to demolish the enemy's machines.

The eastern shore of Connecticut is the territory of seafarers and one of the towns is the prime whaling port. Along the edge of the sea, the land is a delight where the town is quiet and peaceful with the life hidden between the walls of the homes. It is a site of country living. There is no life at night. The streets are abandoned by cars until the wee hours of the morning. I was uneasy. I was used to busy nights and the sound of the hustle and bustle of the city. I was raised in a big city where everything happening was major—good or bad. It was a way of life. I had a difficult time adjusting to the life that I never knew before. But I was good in acceptance and knowing that animate existence in the stillness of life was possible.

It was a Sunday when I flew to New York and had a connecting flight to Groton. I was in a small plane enough to fit about half a dozen flyers. I could hear the roaring engine while the plane was getting ready to take-off. Soon, we were up in the sky with the golden amber across the pathway above the sea. The flight was noisy, scary and sickening, literally, because of the turbulent condition. I could not see any terrain or outline of streets, avenues or the form of man-made structures. I did not enjoy the scenery as I felt dizzy.

After we landed, I was confused and vertiginous. I sat down for about an hour before I could find my direction. It was not my favorite flight and it became the last flight via the rural area. I was bewildered of how I would make it. The airport is minuscule compared to the city airport that I am used to. I picked up my eight (8) pieces of matching luggage and I felt funny. Everyone gave me a look like, "Who is she?" I am really nobody. I happened to be in a lay-back country.

In the airport, there are four business counters—two for car rentals and two for small airline offices. There are no skycaps or taxicabs lined-up in a special parking area by the front of the airline building. Whenever someone needs a cab, a phone service does the job. It means several minutes of waiting. It was all right except, to my surprise, the other passengers who called for a cab were waiting for the same cab.

The driver had a route accessible to his convenience. Anyway, I would not know the difference between the long and short routes since I was new in the area. One passenger was dropped off in one hotel. When we finally got to my scheduled hotel, I noticed there was no bellboy. I requested the cab driver to bring my luggage to the front desk. He agreed with a hefty tip. I checked in and asked the receptionist how my eight pieces of luggage would make it to the room on the second floor since there was no elevator. She said, I had to wait for the cook's break so he could help me. I could not believe the event I was living through.

I made a taxicab reservation for an early Monday morning pick-up. That morning, I went to the hotel lobby fifteen (15) minutes before the appointed time. A cab driver arrived with a passenger and parked the cab. He sat for a few minutes. Then, another gentleman approached the driver and got in the same cab. Still, they did not leave. I kept looking at my watch. The time kept ticking away. The cab passengers looked worried so the cab driver got out of the cab and went in the hotel lobby. He spotted me and asked me if I was waiting for a reserved cab. He had been waiting for a lady passenger. I told him, I reserved a cab but I did not expect a cab with passengers would pick me up. He explained the riding arrangement in the area. I told him I thought I would not have to share a ride if I reserved the cab a day before the scheduled time. I was wrong. From where I came from, we did not share rides with strangers.

It was a spring crispy day. The slight breeze kept me alive. The company I worked for had miles and miles of office buildings alongside the Thames River feeding to the Long Island Sound. The hilly streets gave me a sense of new belonging. I walked through the quiet avenue as I changed from building to building. To get work started, I had to go to the company's main office which was the only accessible building that did not require a security badge. Everyone is wearing a picture-badge which can be checked by the assigned gate security guard anytime. I was sent to the company's hospital to pass the physical exams. Then I was briefed, tested, lectured, and granted the security clearances by the Department of Defense (DOD) and Department of Energy (DOE).

The weather did not cooperate. The treacherous rain was pouring, drenching everything. It seemed the thunderstorm and lightning kept it going. It was dark while it rained all day. Being my first day at work, I did not appreciate the rain. I did not have any rain paraphernalia. I was soaked. There was nothing I could do. When I started work, I was glamorous but when work ended, I looked like a shaggy dog. I had the taste of New England weather in the spring.

The shipyard is vast and it includes a school building, hospital, and several buildings utilized to complete a submarine construction. It is a common sight to see the workers and the machines attack tons of steel to bring about a submarine. I was introduced to the submarine engineering world by visiting the submarine mock-up (wooden sub) and the areas important to my job.

As a Project Engineer, my job provides technical assistance for the resolution of problems concerning structural modifications, repair, and overhaul work in submarine nuclear propulsion plants; manages and supervises projects in production for the accomplishment of alteration work packages; performs liaison work with Naval Sea Systems Command (NSSC), naval shipyards, and prime contractors; provides an order of magnitude and period of performance work estimate for assigned projects based on the work scopes; and provides technical and administrative direction to ensure that nuclear quality systems and controls are adequate.

Included in my job are: performing inspections, engineering studies, and visiting the nuclear submarine to test the accuracy of certain nuclear areas that are under construction. Working on the different phases of submarine construction involves dealing with welders, grinders, machinists, riggers, testers, and radiation monitors. Various classes of submarines need a response to liaison action requests (LAR). Occasionally, I had to go to the state where the submarine being renovated was docked and made important technical decisions. I spent eight (8) years doing the job. It is special and it exhilarates me.

For the first two (2) weeks of the job, I was living in a hotel, subsidized by the company. But I had to move out to more permanent housing. I found a house in a quiet residential place a little far from the shipyard. It was a big contemporary house with three (3) floor levels, four (4) bedrooms, and two (2) bathrooms. Living alone in a big place like that scares me. I could not sleep at night. There was no single light on the streets and the houses were far apart. All I heard were weird sounds from various birds, insects, animals and other kinds.

After a week, I could no longer stay. A friend recommended another place where the owner was leasing a second floor apartment with two (2) bedrooms, a bathroom, and a common kitchen/dining room. It is a beautiful place where the scenery is Long Island Sound. The north, south and east exposures of the house are the Sound. Relaxingly, I brushed the wind with a sense that I was in the middle of the ocean. I was calm, serene, and tranquil.

Several months later, I moved to an apartment on a hilltop, set on a large wooded site with various elevations. It was my niche. The top apartment was contemporary and had a balcony overlooking the trees, greens, and the swimming pool where I spent quiet moments, in the morning or evening, doing a few laps. The area was quiet and the streets were well-lit.

Prior to moving to New England, I had a bachelor's degree in engineering. After I was settled into my job, I went back to (evening) school for my master's degree. Then went on to MBA. The MBA courses took me away. They were so interesting, I was so wound-up I could not sleep at night. It seems the day is short. I wish the twenty-four (24) hours a day is longer than real.

The night sets me in a melancholy mood. My borrowed time seems to glide away as the stream flows through. Slumberland breaks the fruition of my desired task. Whenever I close my eyes, it seems I lose several promises. But I have to accept the quiescence—just to function. I am pleased with the outcome of my schooling, even though I have to drive fifty (50) miles to go to school and another fifty (50) miles to get home. At ten (10) o'clock past, the night seemed young and I lived by that. I enjoyed driving alone for many miles because it gave me time to reflect on things that happened each day. I found reasons to understand the ideas that came along. I like that. I did not feel decadent. At the same time, driving alone was good therapy to my tired and busy mind.

Because of a sudden emotional upset, I had to withdraw from graduate school indefinitely. I discuss the resumption in a later chapter.

2

AN EXPERIENCE
OF A LIFETIME

IT IS A BALMY AUTUMN IN NEW ENGLAND with the trees covered with golden and reddish leaves across the hilly thoroughfare. Within the borders are the deep river valleys and a meandering shoreline that give way to sandy beaches. It is an overture to the quiet snow of winter.

On a cool day in September 1991, I was going home from work with my friend, Tom. I seldom ride with him because a lot of times, I have a school class. It was an atypical day. I could not describe my feelings about myself. I felt numbness in my right hand. It was an eerie feeling that I never felt before. Tom thought I was famished. He knows when I get involved with my work, I forget to eat. I assured him that I would have my dinner as soon as I got home. The whole time he was driving, I was quiet and sorting out my feelings. We got home and I was astounded. I could not move. I was trying to get out of the car but the right side of my body was paralyzed. He carried me to the house and called 911.

An ambulance and a couple of fire trucks came. I was in a daze. I saw a lot of people in the house. I did not know where they came from. There was no fire but they were there. I was taken to the hospital while my head was spinning. It was killing me, so much so, it was unbearable. We made it to the hospital

14

in less than a few minutes and the paramedics rushed me to the emergency room. I was somnolent. Two sharp pains and I had a sudden loss of consciousness. Then, I slipped into a coma, an abnormal deep stupor. I was comatose for forty-eight (48) hours and my survival rate was fifty-fifty. People in the intensive care unit (ICU) were lamenting and the patients showed a profound hopelessness. It never occurred to me that I could be a case.

To Tom, it was a traumatic experience and he learned a frightening development. The doctors told him that they could not touch me because I was massively intracerebral hemorrhaging. And the brain was vulnerable to the slightest damage. They were watching the activity occurring at that moment. It was crucial, they could not tell when I would come out of a coma. I had a life-threatening and full-blown stroke to the left of my brain where the essential supply of oxygen, with other nutrients, was upset and the nerve cells in the central area were dying. However, some of the injured cells immediate to the dead cell area were saved.

A molecular pump fails to control the concentration of sodium, potassium, and water inside and outside the brain cells. Because of this, the cells become swollen with water. In less than an hour, the injured brain cells start releasing toxins that destroy and impair endangered brain cells in the stroke area. One of the toxins is glutamate, a salt of glutamic acid which is an amino acid formed in the hydrolysis of proteins. Glutamic acid is the only amino acid that is metabolized by the brain. Glutamate joins nearby cells and allows deadly quantities of calcium to flow into the cell and possibly, releasing highly reactive free radicals, destroying the brain cells. Free radicals are molecules consisting of an odd number of electrons, which is an extremely minute particle with a negative electrical charge that revolves about the central core or nucleus of an atom. They cause the loss of tissue elasticity and weaken the cellular integrity. Too much calcium destroys the cells instantly. Hours after the stroke starts, the cells die increasingly upon the resumption of blood flow.

I had a spontaneous deep left thalamic to subependymal hemorrhage, cerebrovascular accident (CVA), a very dense right hemiparesis, severe expressive aphasia and apraxia, a large acute left temporal and parietal hematoma with intraventricular extension, a mass effect, ambulation dysfunction and cognitive impairment. The uncontrollable hemorrhage in my brain was caused by the rupture of a sac formed by a swelling at the weak point of an artery, like an inflated balloon reaching its limit. The dilatation is known as *aneurysm*, the smallest injury or wound in the human body. It is not a common cause of a stroke, only about ten (10) percent of the stroke victims have aneurysms, a congenital defect where the rupture spot of the blood vessel is existing at birth. I was predisposed to stroke, sooner or later. It is associated with stress or high blood pressure which ruin the blood vessel as it stretches.

Aneurysm is like a time-bomb waiting to explode. It can pop anywhere. It can be determined by magnetic resonance imaging (MRI), which shows the brain, its tissues, and nerves. The hydrogen atom of the fat and water content of the body is the basis of the magnetic force and radio waves used in the MRI. The machine sends radio signals that excites the hydrogen atoms and absorbs the waves as the nuclei spray energy.

At the moment of the activity, my blood pressure was under control. There was a time when my blood pressure was extremely low, close to the bottom of the scale, that I was considered dying. The pressure of the blood against the blood vessel walls, especially the arteries, is referred to as the blood pressure, which consists of systolic and diastolic. When the left ventricle (lower chamber) of the heart contracts and pushes the blood through the body, it is systolic. The pressure when the ventricle relaxes and fills with blood is diastolic. The top

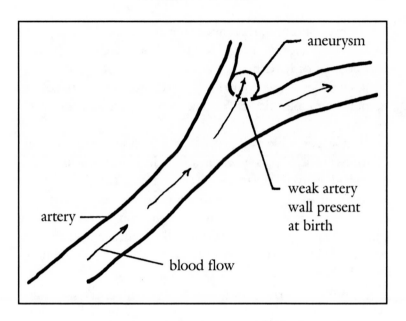

Aneurysm balooning-out with blood

pressure is known as systolic and the bottom pressure as diastolic.

Blood pressure is affected by the strength of the heartbeat, volume of blood in the body, elasticity of the blood vessels, age and general health of the person, where depression plays a role. Depression has a quantifiable effect on the sympathetic nervous system, which controls the heart rate and blood pressure. Depressed people have elevated levels of the stress hormones cortisol and norepinephrine, which can increase the heart rate and blood pressure. The stress hormones can also encourage platelets to clump together and form clots, constrict arteries, and trigger irregular heartbeats. High levels of these stress hormones, chronically, may increase the damage due to the wear and tear of the blood vessels and heart. Also, it may contribute to heart rhythm disturbances.

In my condition, there was no warning sign. I was physically fit with a lot of energy. My blood pressure was regular. I had no sign of hardening of arteries. I was not smoking. My cholesterol level was controlled. I exercised, ran, walked, did aerobics and Nordic track. Under no circumstances was I overweight.

While a horrible experience was occurring, I had no family relations around. My son was in school in France and my sisters and brother lived in various states and countries. Tom made connections with my son and sisters to inform them of the accident. I was in the ICU and no one could determine my plight. My family and friends from other states flew in and met each other in the hospital between tears and emotional numbness. It was a sudden blow to my son.

Halfway to dying, the ensuing days displayed a good sign while I struggled for life. At that powerful moment, another level broke through and woke me up from a coma. It was a miracle. Nobody can fathom the joy of being alive. But not for a long while. I could not see, speak, read, or move. Everything was blurred. My right vision was slashed in half, a blind spot in my right eye, and the right half of my body was paralyzed from head to toe.

It was an enormous undertaking. Not knowing the various changes I was facing, I was deprived of sensation and movement in the physical and mental abilities. I was in terrible shock. I was stupefied. I could not believe the things that happened to me. For a while, I had no certainties in my life. I wanted to understand my emotion. I was in a coma and I came back as an entity. I believe in the monotheistic creator and ruler of the universe. So I question, "Why did He bring me back to life?" When I was not hurting, I came back. But when I was back, I was suffering. I meditated to find myself.

I was transferred to critical care unit (CCU). The stroke affected every significant part of my body—the senses, thoughts, memory, and speech. I was a basket case. The neurological damage was of great extent, it was difficult to endure. My body balance was zilch as two therapists tried to pull my body vertically, and it dropped like an accordion. I was very weak. I thought the day would not come when I could understand what was happening. Day after day, I was stretched on my bed, forcefully.

One day, a nurse pulled me out of the bed and wheeled me to a shower room. I was still numbed and dazed. The nurse was good. She was like giving a shower to a dead person. Lifeless as I was, I gaped as I was showering. My hair was falling in bulk, as the water touched it. I was horrified. On second thought, I should not care less because I did not know how long I was going to be around. Although I was alive, I was in a vegetated state. I was breathing but I could not sense a lot of things. I was more an illusion.

I was fed in bed with either a spoon or fork but half of the food landed on my clothes. Half of my mouth was paralyzed. The feeling was not there to sense the presence of any object. As days went on, feeding myself improved by learning to use dining utensils with my unsteady left hand. I was dominantly a right-handed person. But I became helpless like a child trying to place the spoon in the mouth, sideways. I did not realize I could not see half of the food plate.

Day after day, my son visited me alone with an overwhelming defeat. The consternation on his face showed the difficulty of accepting that something serious happened to me. I could not talk but he wanted to communicate with me the way we used to.

He said, "Mom, I know you cannot talk but you can hear me. Wave your left hand if you do. I want to tell you that the doctor talked to me about your condition. He explained the situation. You are alive but he cannot do anything more for you. He said you will be there like a living vegetable and he advised me to finish school and to do what I think is best for us. Knowing you, I think I know exactly what you want me to do. I will ask you a question and if you understand me, wave to me. If your answer is yes, nod your head as a sign of assent. But if your answer is no, shake your head from side to side. My question is: Do you want me to go back to France to finish my studies?"

I nodded. He hugged me and left the room. A few minutes later, he came back and asked me the same question. I nodded again, he hugged me and left once again. Another few minutes later, he showed up again and said, "Mom, I want to be sure that we are still connected so, I will ask you again the same question. Do you really want me to go back to France to finish my schooling?"

I replied the same way. I nodded clearly and showed my left hand with a good-bye sign. Then he said, "O.K. I am leaving for France tomorrow."

I nodded. He kissed me and hugged me. He was sad but I knew he was glad that he was doing what I wanted him to do. My sisters were against my son's leaving, but none of them understood our feelings for each other.

In a few days, I was transferred to a regular hospital ward. I pondered about life, what it was going to be like, what I was going to do, and what changes there would be in my life. I did not have time to be depressed because I could feel the intensity of the challenge I was facing. I had to plan the logistics of the conflict which I considered an active hostility to my physical and emotional body. I had to fight. But, how? I wondered how long I was going to be in this situation. Not knowing about stroke, I was not aware of the permanency of my disability.

Although I had two eyes, I could only see with one eye. Stroke had caused a visual disturbance that left me with the inability to see the full visual area. It is a complete *hemianopia*, the blindness of half of the field of vision in one eye. It amounts to seeing everything half. For example, when I was looking at a newspaper, I could not see the right side of it. I thought I could just lean my head on the right side, but it did not work. Everything I saw in front of me was cut off vertically in the middle, blacked-out on one side. Any sentence in the newspaper had no continuation. I had a limited tunnel vision and in any text, all the words jumped all over the place.

I was worried because nobody could tell me if I could read again. It was a phase in my life where I needed to look ahead. There was no looking back because that life was gone and nothing could bring it back. There were zillions of questions in my mind but, there were no answers. Can I learn to recoup the losses in my being? Is it possible?

My inability to speak made my daily existence placid. I was saying only two words—"I come." I was stoical and yet, whenever I glanced around me, I relished the beautiful flowers and wreaths, get-well cards, stuffed animals, books, tapes, religious cards and images, gracing the hospital room. The unoccupied bed in my room was filled with flowers from other parts of the nation. My heart was warmed by the many meaningful friends and acquaintances who cared. At that moment of greatest emotional impact, I was touched deeply.

I stared at the blue sky and focused on what became of me. I was sad and at the same time I tried to analyze the events in my life. This is a reality—a new beginning. I feel the loss of driving my car and the view of the physical and normal life. What is there for me? I could not write or talk to my friends, just to say "thank you for remembering me." Do I have a future? Do I have a purpose in life and on earth? Or am I exanimate?

With my deficit, slowly I learned to sit in a chair. As my half-body was paralyzed, my body weight was not balanced. I could not lean on my right side because I would fall at the tip of a hat. The right half of my body had no strength and weight control.

One day, a nurse left me alone in the hospital room toilet, but in a few seconds, I fell. I could not move and my paralyzed right leg was twisted on the floor. I tried to reach the buzzer to signal my exigency but, it was too far. I yelled as loud as I could, but nobody was around to hear me. It took, at least, forty-five (45) minutes before a nurse showed up. I was perspiring and helpless. She was petrified where she found me. My right leg was bruised and she tried to lift me out of that bind, but she could not. At one-hundred ten (110) pounds, I was not heavy. She went out of the room to get some help. Perhaps, I was in physical pain but my right leg lost its power to feel and move. Being lifeless, it is the tendency of an atrophied muscle to have no strength due to lack of energy.

Each day, I could feel the minuscule improvement. Due to the death of numerous brain cells, my brain was still swollen as proved by the CAT (Computerized Axial Tomography) scan, which produced a cross-sectional view of the anatomical part being examined from x-ray data. I spent most of the days in the hospital ward staring at the scenery through the window pane. It seemed I was in a cage. The coldest season of the year was bleak and the road was icy. Nevertheless, I missed the winter storm and walking on the wintry streets. I enjoy the sight of snowfall.

One morning, a nurse came to my room with a packet of Fleet soda and rested it on the table. Fleet soda is for enema and its trade name is sodium bi-phosphate. I ignored it because I did not have a need for it. My bowel movements have always been regular. I remember having Fleet soda when I was a young girl. I hate it.

All of a sudden the nurse instructed me to lie down on the bed to apply the Fleet's enema. I was astounded. I just moved my bowels a few minutes ago. Every morning the nurse sat me on the toilet bowl. But she never told me that she was recording I had a bowel movement problem. It was not true. My lower intestine was cleaned by a routine movement. However, it is my habit to flush the toilet as soon as I move. Because of that, I refused to have an enema. This is a good example of bad communication, whether having or not having aphasia.

One day, I was summoned to the hospital's conference room by the hospital administrator, lawyer, and therapist, to explain to me the importance of probate. Although I could hear what they were saying, I could not respond because I could not talk or write. I was sad. Although I was alive, my brain could not process the messages and verbalize whatever I wanted to say. The processing of the messages was not close to the brain activity.

A few days later, the same group of people came and had a meeting on the same topic. They wanted to be sure that I agreed on what we talked about previously. The probate court was concerned about my ability to handle my personal and financial affairs. Because of that, the court wanted to appoint a conservator of my estate and person—to oversee my property and medical needs, food, clothing, personal hygiene, housing, and protection from physical abuse.

I recommended Tom to handle my estate because he was aware of most of my accounts. He became the conservator and guardian, since he was willing and able to carry on the duties involving the management and inventory of all my real and personal properties and assets. He obtained an appraisal of the fair market value of my property and bank accounts, as of the date of his appointment. The bank accounts were transferred to the name of my estate and the financial institutions and/or corporations of my assets were notified of the conservator's appointment.

My income payments were directed to the conservator of my estate, who procured a Fiduciary's Probate Certificate. He acted on the judge's decree and every month, he recorded all my accounts, bills, and payments which he submitted to the probate court. It is not an easy job to be a conservator of an estate. There are certain requirements to accomplish which include a probate lawyer and fees, bond, court hearing, recording and certifying copies of documents, mailing certified or registered notices, inventory reports and accounting of estate. It was his duty to pay my bills and taxes and consult the court prior to the sale of assets and before spending anything other than routine payments.

After two months in the hospital, I was transferred to a health care center where I spent four (4) months of my life. I had mixed emotions about staying in another place other than the hospital. Was I being prepared for a permanent home for the aged or for the infirm? I did not think it would happen to me that soon. The hospital is not a convalescent home. I needed time to regain my physical and mental abilities. I was not capable of going home, yet. The health care center was appropriate for my needs with amenities. It has a good size therapy room, library, recreation center, shower and sauna rooms, whirlpool, gift shop, barber and beauty shops, and laundry room. The place is situated in a sprawling hill by the bay with acreage greens. It was a quiet place conducive to thinking and learning.

The health care center has a well-rounded program for the patients. It includes ceramic arts, painting, cooking, sing-a-longs, poetry, story reading, and watching movies. There was a party for every occasion. I did not join the activities. There were other things I wanted to do. While most people were having a listening activity, I went to the front office to borrow a pair of scissors, needle, and thread.

With my left hand, I cut and hemmed the bottom of my new pants. It took me several hours to finish one pant leg but I enjoyed doing it. I was pleased with my feat, so I went a little farther. I had a torn security blanket that I kept for years, to keep me warm and secured wherever I was—in the airplane or at home. Each time I looked at the frayed edge, it disturbed me. I straightened the side, clipped the edge, rolled and hemmed it. It was a little complicated with one hand but, I was determined. It is my nature to finish whatever I start. In two sittings, I finished my blanket. It is a sign that I can be useful.

At the rehab center, almost all patients have to be helped in the washroom—to urinate or move bowels. At around lunch time, it was difficult to get help. Some patients had unpleasant accidents. I did not have a problem with that. However, I decided to do a project—how to go to the washroom by myself. In my wheelchair, I went to the washroom, closed the door and analyzed my situation. I studied the layout of the toilet, hand-rails, and the sink. I figured the length of the rail from the edge of the toilet bowl and the exact location of my left leg and arm in relation to the equipments. I took note of the distances of the four walls from each other. In case I fall or slip, I should know what to do.

I stayed in that room for a good ten (10) minutes, to plan the embarkation which was a big undertaking. I was concerned because the right half of my body was not cooperating with my left half. I already experienced falling from the toilet bowl. So, I had to be very careful. By studying the layout, I was psyched to take care of myself. I believe that anything is possible with a strong mind.

Centralizing my interest, I did the project step by step. I was satisfied. I practiced a few times even though I was wobbly. I told myself, I could do it. I was proud. From that time on, I have been doing it alone. It seemed nobody noticed the habitual hygiene routine. I was wrong.

A nurse asked me, "Who has been helping you in the washroom lately?" She wanted to know if the other nurse was doing it.

I answered, "No one."

She was very surprised. She asked me to show her how I did it. I did a replay into sight and she was impressed.

My independence followed me through. Everyone of us was scheduled to take a towel bath every night with the aid of a nurse assistant. I felt I could do it by myself. I asked for a nightgown and some towels. The assistant was leery about letting me do it; hence, she watched me and she was pleased. After the patients were cleaned, they were put to bed. I had an advantage. I could do it anytime. That's the beauty of being independent.

One night, I was in bed early even though I was not ready to sleep yet. I decided to get something from my dresser, which was next to the right side of my bed. Because my right side was paralyzed, I had to get up. I sat down on the edge of the bed and positioned myself to transfer to my wheelchair to reach for something with my left hand. For some reason, I blacked out and hit my head on the wheelchair and the floor. I passed out. I hit my head hard, I awakened my roommate. She yelled for help and because I was unconscious, she thought I was dead. She was in tears while she got the nurse and the assistants rushing to our room. They picked me up from the floor and laid me on the bed. In a few minutes, I was conscious with a huge black eye and a swollen cheek. It took two months for the bruise to come down and the lump on my cheek was eternal.

As I survived the stroke, a distressing sensation in my chest developed. It started as an annoying pain every now and then. The muscle in my chest was extremely hard like a rock. It seemed someone punched or boxed me. The pain worsened. I was given a pain-killer at night to make me relax and sleep. The drug relieved the pain, but it did not cure the ailment. I could not understand why the doctors were not concerned about the pain. Although they were aware of it. Knowing it was worse than before, they seemed ambivalent about it. Was it normal for stroke victims to have this kind of pain? Will the pain go away in time? I was ailing for a couple of months. The pain and its area increased rather than decreased. Finally, the doctor gave me a shot of a pain-killer but, it did not assuage the pain.

In consulting a couple of doctors, the physical therapist administered the use of TENS (Transcutaneous Electrical Nerve Stimulator) to control chronic and post-traumatic pain.

It was believed to be effective in different kinds of pain, mild to severe. The TENS electrodes were attached to the end of a device chord. To avoid skin irritation, a protector was applied on the body where the contact came together. The battery was placed in the micro-computer circuitry, and the TENS was adjusted to the degree of pain. The machine was turned on or off depending upon the intensity of the electrical signals. The fixture on my body alleviated the chest pain as long as I was wearing it. That perturbed me. I felt, in time I would be immune to the electrodes that no amount of time would make the machine work for me.

Medically stable, I was transferred to an acute rehabilitation hospital with comprehensive programs to increase my functional improvement and my independency. It was also intended to evaluate if it was possible for me to go back to the engineering job I had. I was tested more than once. I presented problems with abstract elementary calculations.

One of the wings of the hospital was for Young Stroke Educational Group, where I was situated. The main attraction of the hospital, not to mention the other medical features, is a huge therapeutic department housing the hydro, physical, occupational, speech, and outpatient therapies. It is impressive because the goal of maximizing physical and cognitive therapies are attainable in this environment.

The intensive rehabilitation was enforced with eight (8) hours of formal and individualized treatment each day, seven (7) days a week. It encompassed speech, physical and occupational therapies, vocational counseling, cognition, community skills, and independent living. The program was hectic but I was driven to learn. Recovery was foremost in my mind. The stroke destroyed the very important aspect of my being. The process of knowing, awares the perception, reasoning, judgment, intuition, and memory. Re-learning these skills have an underlying strength that survives the knowledge underneath.

The first thing the rehab physician undertook vigorously was the elimination of TENS. I detected my dependency on the electronic device because I was in pain when it was removed from my body. In place of the machine, he put me on rigid stretch exercises. Upward from my rib cage, my breasts were stone-stiff that I could not feel or move the flexibility of my skin. With the pain came the body muscle tone.

The tone has a normal elasticity and resiliency. However, the muscle of my half-paralyzed body was constricted. It appeared the length of the right extremities were shorter than my left. My right leg was so stiff that it faced sideways. Because of the presence of the eccentric tone, the rigidness directed the extremities in the wrong course. For instance, when I wanted to walk from point A to point B, I had to go to point C first. The tone forced me to develop an elliptical form rather than a straight line.

The physiatrist, a physician who specialized in physical medicine, took over my leg problem, attempting to normalize the physical condition. To ease the consistency of muscle contraction, a nerve block system was utilized by the application of a regional anesthesia to prevent sensory nerve impulses and to avoid touching centers of consciousness. After the process, my leg and thigh were put in a cast to train the correct position of the extremities. However, in less than an hour, I was in excruciating pain. It is one of the unbearable pains that I did not want to experience again. By the doctor's order, the nurses had to take the cast out but re-placed it in the evening for as long as I could bear it, to ease the healing. The longer I kept the cast on, the endurance got better. In conjunction with physical therapy, my leg improved.

When the muscles are in a steady state of contraction, they are in tone. The tone in my body controls the pain, in a bad note. Due to the stroke, the tone loses its normal position in the body. It tends to shrink and stiffens the muscles. The tone can resist a force for a long period of time without change in length. However, the flexion condition ruins the physical form and function of a particular part of the body. For example, a newborn child does not have body tone. The normal elastic firmness is needed to help the child hold the head upright. As time goes on, the body becomes resilient enough so that the child can raise the head upright for a comfortable length of time. The tone in my body has been botched up by the stroke. It has to be restored in the right places.

The rehabilitation hospital has an interesting stroke support group program which I joined one evening. We introduced ourselves to everyone. A gentleman sitting next to me spoke and poured out his feelings about what stroke did to him. He was despondent and mentioned that he tried to kill himself three different occasions, after he had a stroke. But he failed each time. He showed us his scarred wrist and with a disappointing sound, he looked at me as I was staring at him in disbelief. He said, "Maybe, you have not achieved anything in life. I did. The stroke takes away everything I live for. What do you do?"

For some incredible reason, I was able to talk (slowly) and said, "I am shocked. How can you even think of killing yourself? Do you really want to know my accomplishments in life?"

He replied, "Yes. What did you do before you had the stroke?"

I started telling him that I worked as a nuclear engineer but, he was taken aback. However, I continued saying, "I am sad at what I went through. Nevertheless, life is not over yet. I believe I have a purpose on earth."

A few days later, he came to my hospital ward and said, "I will never forget you. Life has a meaning since I met you. I will never try to kill myself again. I promise you that much."

He was touched. With tears in his eyes.

3

THE BRAIN COMPLEXITY

PERHAPS THE MOST EXTRAORDINARY ORGAN—the brain, encephalon or *cerebrum* (in Latin)—is bilaterally symmetrical. It is the organ of the mind, the source of human thoughts and creativity, and the command center of the human body, which is, by far, the most astonishing mechanism on earth. The brain weighs about three (3) pounds and it has two halves, the right and the left hemispheres, connected by *corpus callosum*, a thick bridge of fibers, situated deep inside the cerebrum. It was proved that the two halves of the brain are two separate cerebrums and each one can be trained to do something independent of the other.

The cerebrum is attached to the *cerebellum*, Latin for little brain, which is connected to *medulla oblongata*, an enlarged part of the spinal cord in cranium, the portion of the skull that enclosed the brain. The cerebellum drives the motor fibers to the thalamus, brainstem, and other structures. It manages information regarding the body, arms, and leg positions. The brain and the spinal cord, being connected to each other, have one nervous system and both organs control the human body's motions and senses. (A new development: The cerebellum is not only controlling the body movements but also processing various sensory information. For instance, the feel of real objects. When the eyes are closed and a particular key is reached, the cerebellum helps differentiate the house key from the car key.)

30

The brainstem, an extension of the spinal cord, consists of the *midbrain*, *medulla* (meaning "marrow") and *pons* (meaning "bridge"). The midbrain has centers receiving messages from the inner ear and eyes and it assists in coordinating movement and muscle tone. The medulla and pons control the heartbeat, blood pressure, breathing and the signals to swallow, sneeze, and laugh. The *thalamus*, meaning "inside chamber," is an inner compartment in the brain coordinating the nerve impulses relating to the senses of sight, hearing, touch, and taste. It consists of two small egg-shaped structures, one for each cerebral hemisphere. An injury to the thalamus causes disturbance of sensation and partial or complete paralysis of one side of the body.

The outer layer of the human brain, which is the most significant section, is called the *cerebral cortex*, meaning "shell." It is the brain's outer covering of cells. Damage to a portion of the cerebral cortex in the left hemisphere negates a person's ability to understand or speak clearly. The skull or *cranium*, covers the cerebral cortex by three membranes—the outermost is *dura mater* (dura meaning hard), the middle is *arachnoid*, and the innermost is the *pia mater* (pia meaning tender).

The cortex, protected from shock by membranes and fluids, has four lobes—occipital, temporal, parietal, and frontal lobes. The *occipital lobe*, located at the back, unifies nerve signals from the eyes, referred to as the visual cortex. An injury to the occipital lobe can cause blindness despite the other part of the visual system not being affected. The *temporal lobes*, one on either side, involve hearing, speech, perception, and memory. Some parts of the temporal lobe damaged by stroke result in aphasia. The *parietal lobe* handles sensory responses and muscle control. An injury to the parietal lobe results to *amorphosysthesis*, a condition where a person is unaware of half of the body. And the *frontal lobe,* across the forehead, is the largest of the four cortical lobes and it unites information from the other lobes of the cerebral cortex. If the frontal lobe is ruined, the individual is extremely distracted by an irrelevant activity and loses the central point of attention.

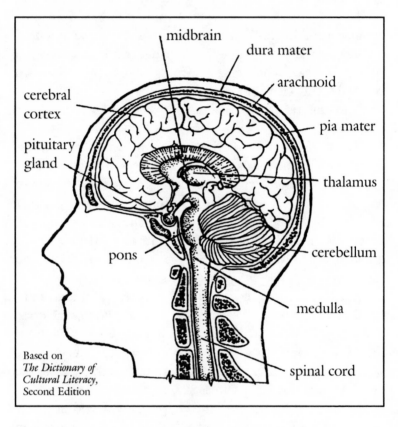

Brain

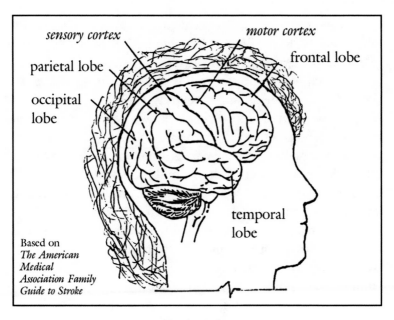

Brain Lobes

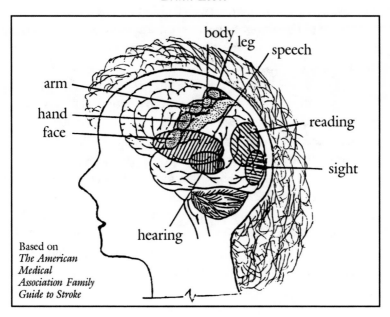

Motor Cortex

After the cardiovascular accident, I wanted to understand what went on in the brain. The brain has about one-hundred (100) billion nerve cells or *neurons*, the essential cells of a nerve center. Each nerve cell has a cell wall called *plasma membrane* and it has as many as one-thousand (1,000) connections or *synapses,* the point of junction between two neurons in a neutral path and the gap between a neuron and the dendrites of another neuron. The gap across the synapses is only twenty-five nanometers (25 nm or 25 millionth of a millimeter).

The nerve center is a group of nerve cells adjacent to one another and acting together in the performance of some functions. The neurons connect the body parts and organs to the central nervous system which carry impulses, a progressive wave of electric and chemical activity along a nerve fiber that stimulates or inhibits the action of a muscle, gland, or other nerve cell, from one part of the body to another.

Outside the central nervous system is the peripheral nervous system. It includes the twelve (12) pairs of cranial nerves, thirty-one (31) pairs of spinal nerves, and their branches to the entire body. Each nerve contains *afferent fibers* which carry signals to the central nervous system and *efferent fibers* which carry signals away from the central nervous system. It also includes all the sensory nerves, the sympathetic and parasympathetic nerves. Andreas Vesalius (1514-64), a Belgian anatomist, made a dissection of human cadavers to make an illustration of the human body's network of peripheral nerves.

A neuron has three (3) main elements—cell body, axon, and dendrites. The *cell body* is a small mass made up of a central nucleus encircled on all sides by cytoplasm, a protoplasm of a cell outside the nucleus. Protoplasm is the living matter of all cells and tissues. From the cell body are the axon and dendrites. The shape of the nerve cells are irregular and the fibers are more like the branches of a tree, known as *dendrites*. It receives messages from other neurons.

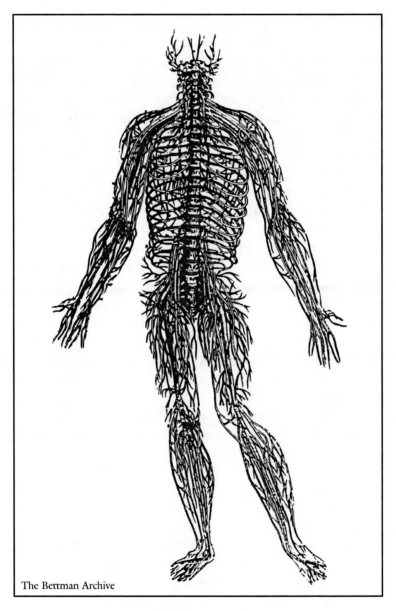

The Bettman Archive

A peripheral nerve network
illustrated by Andreas Vesalius (1514-64)

An *axon*, which sends out chemical messages to other neurons, is a long, thin, and straight fiber that ends in a synapse. Axon is capable of conducting nerve impulses intensified by the myelin sheath that encompasses it. Myelin, a fatty substance, is a natural electrical insulator that protects the axon from interference by other nearby nerve impulses. Within the cell body is the nucleus which contains *deoxyribonucleic acid* (DNA). Nucleic acid, shown in chromosomes of the nuclei of cells, is the chemical foundation of heredity and the carrier of genetic information for all organisms excluding the *ribonuclei acid* viruses. Ribonucleic acid controls protein synthesis in all living cells and takes the place of DNA in certain viruses. DNA cells are damaged by free radicals.

A stroke destroys some neurons and it cuts off the neural ability to contact the other cells. However, the brain is resilient that another neuron takes over the dead cells and the injured brain begins building a new network of neurons. The network expands to the remainder of the nervous system in the body to supply the brain of information about the neighboring environment. A stroke victim can recover the function the brain can gradually restore.

The neuron continuously rebuilds the network. And when the brain is stimulated to interact in the outside environment, it rebuilds itself rapidly. There are some cases whereby the brain works in a different way. If the brain is not properly stimulated, it atrophies and its neural connection dries up. Mental and physical activities may strengthen the network connections between brain cells. The brain stem supports all brain activities and its axon opens out through the entire brain. It has been determined that various experiences are directed to different brain structures and the brain organizes itself and forces to change. It is possible that repetitive exercises stimulate the brain stem. The brain's recovery depends on therapy, motivation and normalizing activities.

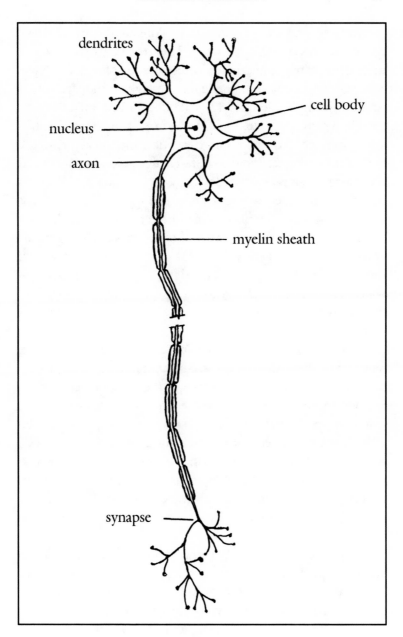

Neuron

At the time I was in a state of prolonged unconsciousness, many things occurred in my brain. The stroke caused damage to the left half of my brain, the left cerebral hemisphere, which was referred to the right hemiplegia, or right hemiparesis. Or simply, the right side paralysis. This area acts on language, speech, writing, science, logic, and complex mathematics. It is also associated with the positive emotion and the ability of the lips, cheeks, tongue, and throat, to change positions swiftly. At the same time, it is associated with *dysarthria*, an impairment of the tongue or other muscles essential to speech. The weakness appears as a drooping of one side of the face or lips.

The left hemisphere controls the activities of the right side of the body, the same way the right hemisphere controls that of the left side of the body. The right cerebral hemisphere is concerned with spatial relationship, music, art appreciation, simple arithmetic, fantasy, physical activity, and simple use of words.

Pierre Paul Broca, a French surgeon and neuroanatomist, made some discoveries about the brain. He found out that his patients who had a brain damage at the posterior end of the inferior frontal convolution of the cerebral left hemisphere, could not speak intelligibly. *Aphasia* is a neurological condition where the language comprehension and expression are upset by the brain dysfunction affecting the order of articulation related to language production. *Apraxia* is the inability to perform purposive movements although there is no sensory or motor impairment. Apraxiac people are not able to use objects properly.

Broca's aphasic patients showed poor grammar. And his area controlled movement of the tongue, lips, and vocal chords. It was also involved with the ability to use syllables to create meaningful words. I was severely aphasic that I could not speak in any fashion other than telegraphically—short and disconnected sentences. Some words are caught inside the brain yet others, successfully press through.

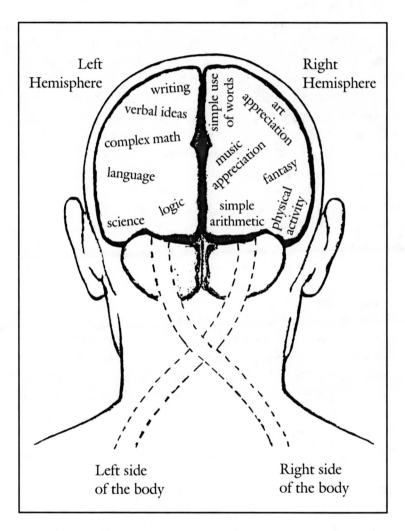

Cerebral Dominance

A typical example of aphasia was when I tried to explain what I did after I took a shower.

I said, "I put away the . . . the . . . thing . . . the thing I used . . . after my thing . . . the thing . . . to dry myself. I hang it. I mean the thing . . . you know. I took a . . . thing . . . and used it. It is a big, soft cloth. Those things."

What a frustration! I could keep on talking but nobody would understand what I was saying. I was at a loss for words, literally. Why couldn't I just say, "I hang the towel after I use it"? This is also an example of *anomia*, a type of aphasia that involves the inability to verbalize the names of objects, people and places. My brain is fluent in the language but, the messages die there. My lips cannot speak the messages my brain delivers.

My aphasic problems are understanding the words and saying it. To be certain that my hearing was absolute, I was given impaired tests several times. I passed all the time. I was willing to find ways to recoup my losses and to find the means to assimilate with normalcy.

Because of my disability, I had to figure out how I could come out of this imbroglio. Something had to be done. The handicapped people have their own way of communicating whether they are deaf, blind, or lame. If a deaf person can lip-read, why can't a stroke victim mind-read? I use the visualization method in more ways than one. The method is the act of viewing or perceiving a picture of an object. To ameliorate my physical predicament, I visualize the movement, gait, leg and arm positions. And I visualize the neurons connecting to other neurons to compensate the dead cells and waking up the idle cells.

To understand words, I lip-read and visualize orthography or spelling words. If I am being spoken to or I have to say something, I focus on words being mentioned as I spell the words in my head. At the same time, I see the orthography in my mind. If I cannot see the spelling of the words, I cannot understand it. Every time I have a chance, I work on the visualization speed. I practice by listening to conversation, television, or radio. It is very helpful to improve my speech, language, and communication.

About a year after my stroke, a piece of my speech came back with impairments in both speech production and speech perception. I had a problem with certain words, phrases, names of objects and grammatical expressions. Some of the problems are literal paraphasic errors, or misuse of spoken words. For instance, I was saying, "acorn" for "unicorn," "punnel" for "funnel," and "backus" for "abacus." The pronunciation of words was indeterminate. In dictation or in taking a direction, the processing in my brain was tough. For instance, instead of "95," I wrote down "59." In direction, I took "right" instead of "left." And I said, "no" when I meant "yes." It was awfully frustrating!

It seemed the stroke caused dyslexia in some survivors. In dyslexia, a patient has normal vision but is not able to interpret written language. It has been considered that the function of the left hemisphere of the brain in dyslexic survivors is different from normal. The sequence of letters and numbers were not easy to remember. When I was counting, the number sequences were juggled. I repeated some numbers which were out of sequence. My lips would say just any number.

I lost the use of language—communication by voice. It was disheartening because I had to start all over again to re-learn reading, writing, and speaking. To be able to read, I had to re-learn to speak first—syllable by syllable. It took a while to work on sentences. Aphasia is not amnesia—a loss of the ability to memorize and recall the stored information. I had memories of retaining and recalling impressions. But I lost the ability to bring certain memories out of the storage. Retention is storing what we learned and recalling is using what has been stored. Fortunately, aphasia's characteristic is to improve memories in time and to embed the shocking events by the help of a stress hormone like adrenaline.

Each day, I trusted that the retention and recalling would improve. I have a problem with following instructions because the processing in my brain was faster than my word development and speech. Whenever I opened my mouth, the words would come out but, it would not make sense. It appeared that my tongue was uncontrollable. In other words, I was speechless. It was not easy to pronounce some polysyllables, foreign words, and technical terms. If I pronounced a word correctly, I could not repeat it. The words and phrases were eluding me and the processing was not available. I had difficulty with producing speech, writing, comprehension, and calculation.

Stroke recovery comes at a snail's pace, but it does happen. I never gave up working on recovery. I practice reading and writing, word syllable by syllable although, I have a blind spot in my right eye. Aphasia messes up communication whether by speech or by writing. When the brain tells me something, often times, I cannot transmit it correctly. The things I hand-write are incoherent, any word will come out. The sentences are grammatically wrong and there are no word articles or prepositions. It is bizarre!

Four (4) years after I had the stroke, I decided to buy a computer to help me read and write and possibly, speed-up my learning ability. I was aware of a reading software so I used it for its purpose. One day, something unusual happened while I was using the computer to write a letter to a friend. My left fingers were punching the right keys to write the correct words and sentences. The computer was transmitting my thoughts while my brain was responding clearly. My brain and the computer were in synch! They were talking. It was an amazing discovery. When I use pen and paper, the sentence structures are grotesque. That's when I decided to write this book.

The following year, I was determined to achieve the MBA degree. When stroke hit me, I was working on the two final courses to graduate. But I had to withdraw and the school put me on a medical leave of absence. There was doubt that my brain would go back to normalcy. I had to find out. I wrote separate letters to the school dean, registrar, admission director and to the professors. I got the approval. I did my research and worked on it with my computer. The glowing sign showed my brain was almost scatheless. Everything fell in the right places. It was great.

The stroke has three types—cerebral thrombosis, cerebral embolism and hemorrhage. *Cerebral thrombosis* is a stroke caused by a blood clot or thrombus that develops in a brain artery. When a brain artery is obstructed by foreign substances or a blood clot, it is a *cerebral embolism* stroke. And when an artery ruptures and the blood goes in and on the surface of the brain, it is known as *hemorrhage* stroke.

It has been ascertained that depressed adults have a fifty (50) percent increased risk of dying from a stroke. They may be prone to stroke because they secrete more stress hormones and depression changes the blood platelet activity. Platelet is a round or oval disk found in the blood of vertebrates and has something to do with blood coagulation.

Although the brain damage is irreversible, there are striking advances and developments to compensate lost faculties. Aneurysm has a new treatment even if it ruptures. By surgery, a chip is place across the base of the aneurysm to close it off. If it is not possible, a bypass is placed around the aneurysm. A very recent treatment is when a radiologist or neurosurgeon detects an aneurysm. Coils are placed inside the aneurysm to obstruct the area.

Under experiment is a new treatment for stroke victims. It dissolves clot to restore the blood flow to the brain. The drug is a building block of cell membranes which lessens cell deaths and gives way to repair the damaged membranes. With this treatment, it limits the amount of brain injury in the first hour after a stroke. However, the treatment has potential risks and benefits. If the right patient were treated, it could prevent lifetime paralysis and other crippling disabilities. On the other hand, if the treatment were given to the wrong patient, it could initiate or precipitate bleeding in the brain that could worsen the stroke.

The neurologists and radiologists have a new discovery. They can watch a stroke in progress killing the brain tissues and observe the shocked neighboring tissues that may be revived with treatment. The neurologist' doctrine that once the adult brain was injured, the recovery was not expected. However, the medical principle and philosophy changed with the advent of new research and technology. A person with stroke symptoms can be placed in magnetic resonance imaging (MRI) to determine the stroke occurrence. The machine shows the stroke within minutes of its attack while the regular MRI techniques cannot detect a stroke until hours after it starts. The first hour is critical because it is during this moment that the shocked neighboring cells die or recover. A new drug is being developed to protect the damaged brain cells from dying.

A subject of argument is the hyperbaric oxygen (HBO) therapy technique to promote healing of new tissues and activate the blood supply of the shocked neurons. Although it has credits in treating burns, gangrene, and flesh-eating bacteria, it is not without risk.

A highly experimental technique is a balloon treatment especially for thrombolytic stroke which is difficult to prevent. That particular stroke is five (5) times more common than the hemorrhagic stroke. In a thrombolytic stroke, arterial debris floats into the brain, sticks in a blood vessel, and has a clot reaction. In the new approach, a plastic-coated balloon-tipped catheter wire is inserted through the groin's incision and a plaque-narrowed carotid artery of the neck and into the brain is steered with the use of a computerized monitor x-ray. Then, the balloon is inflated to spread out the blood vessel for better circulation. However, the system has drawbacks because the brain's blood vessel is thin and narrow and it takes a well-trained doctor in neurology and radiology to successfully perform this new technique.

4

CHALLENGE THE PARADIGM

For seven months, I was in two hospitals and a health care center. I was released to my friend's house, and for the first time, I felt alone and inept. I could no longer do anything I used to do. It appeared that my life was over. I looked at myself and realized that I had to do something. I was existing, but that was all. I had to come to terms with that reality, and from there on I had to finalize my intention of going on with my life.

A couple of years later, inch by inch, I learned to read and write again. I felt I recovered the handling of my personal and business accounts. I could do simple math and understand the basics of my business. Tom was amazed. I regained control of the basic needs. Later on, he requested the court, in writing, to review the need for my conservatorship since he felt I had been restored to capacity. The probate court set a date to schedule a hearing and finally, the court affirmed Tom's request. As a conservator his responsibility cannot be overstated. It was based on trust, confidence, and good faith from both of us. The profit, gain, or benefit in the management of my estate shows the degree of his competency.

The stroke presented me with a difficult aftermath. Due to the stroke, my whole life changed. I used to run or walk outdoors several times a week, alternating with aerobics and Nordic track because the activities relaxed me. But since then, every phase of my active existence had to be rebuilt. Self-range of motion is maintained to avoid muscle pain, stiffness, and abnormal muscle tone. In addition to mobilization for daily activities.

For the shoulders, I raise and shrug the shoulders. For the lateral bending of the shoulder or abduction, I cradle the arms, raise it to shoulder level and move it from side to side. For the flexion or bending of the shoulder, I raise the arm over the head. For the rotation of the shoulder, I push the elbow away from the body. For the extension and flexion of the elbow, I cross the arms, touch the chin, and stretch the elbow all the way. For the forearm supination (facing upward) and pronation (facing downward), I turn the palm up and down. For hand flexion and extension, I grip the palm and bend the wrist back and forth. For the ulna-radius wrist (bone of the forearm), I grip the palm and move it side to side. For the finger flexion and extension, I straighten the fingers and bend them into the palm making a fist. For the thumb abduction, I spread the thumb and the index finger. And finally, for the finger abduction, I spread all the fingers apart and back together. I do each exercise once a day on the count of ten (10).

The doctor at the health care center recommended the use of a cane if I would like to start walking. But, the cane cannot give me a feeling of security. It seems I can fall easily with a cane. I do not trust the implement and I do not want to depend on a "foreign hand." I cannot walk with a cane because I need my only hand to do important things necessary for my day-to-day subsistence. Something has got to give. The cane had to go.

I worked on my body balance. If I could stand steadily for a few minutes, I could handle the balance. I walked holding a cane without touching the floor. I was determined to make it work although my left leg would buckle down at times. Each day, I walked a little farther with the cane off the floor, until I felt confident. Because my right leg is paralyzed, I have to be aware of the direction of my right foot.

*Push the elbow
away from the body.*

*Raise and shrug
the shoulders.*

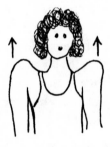

Raise the arms over the head.

Jonathan N. DePaz '97

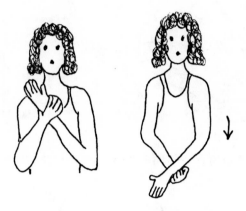

Cross the arms and touch the chin.
Stretch the elbow all the way.

Cradle the arms, raise it to the shoulder level
and move it from side to side.

Jonathan N. DePaz '97

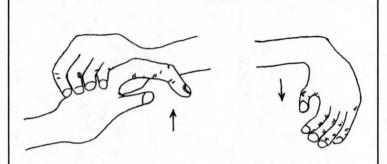

Grip the palm and bend the wrist back and forth.

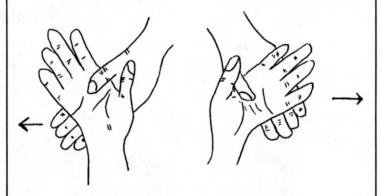

Grip the palm and move it side to side.

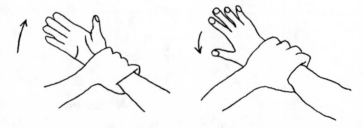

Turn the palm up and down.

Jonathan N. DePaz '97

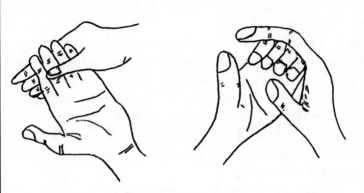

Straighten the fingers and bend them into the palm,
making a fist.

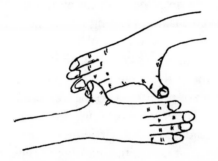

Spread the thumb and the index finger.

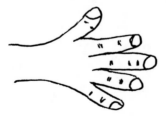

Spread all the fingers apart and back together.

Jonathan N. DePaz '97

My next project was my facial symmetry. The right side of my face is impaired of sensation, unbalanced with the left and has no emotions—no fear, anger, joy or sadness. The face has many small and voluntary muscles that allow us to smile, wink, frown, and make other expressions. In order for the right face to catch up with the level of the left face, I mobilized the right side of my face by a series of facial exercises. I do these exercises in front of a mirror to proportionate the facial symmetry. The weakened facial muscles are strengthened and toned by constant mouth exercises.

I pucker (wrinkle) and purse the lips with a sound and smile widely. With a straw, I blow air by puffing up the cheeks and covering the end of the straw to prevent the air from escaping. I puff one cheek at a time and push the air out with a finger. I pucker the lips while making a kissing sound and pull the lips to one side, one at a time. I smile and hold one corner of the mouth, at the same time, puckering the lips. I do the same on the other side. I move the tongue from end to end and up to down. I put the top of my tongue to the roof of my mouth and place the tongue in cheek while the finger pushes it out. I do the same on the other side. Finally, I circle the tip of the tongue. In these exercises, there is no definite number of repetitions. I do it whenever it is possible.

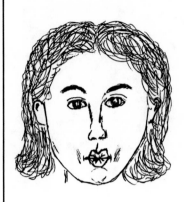

*Pucker lips and say
OOO . . . OOO*

*Smile and say
EEE . . . EEE*

*With puffed cheeks, blow air
through a straw.*

*With puffed up cheeks,
cover the straw with a finger
to stop air.*

Jonathan N. DePaz '96

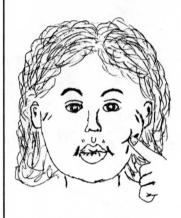

With puffed up cheeks,
push air out with a finger.

Pucker lips
making a kissing sound.

Pucker lips and pull apart one
side, then the other side.

Smile, hold one corner of
the mouth and pucker the lips.
Do the same on the other
corner of the mouth.

Jonathan N. DePaz '96

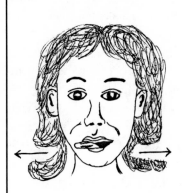

Move the tongue from one corner of the mouth to the other.

Move the tongue up and down.

Position the tongue tip on the roof of the mouth.

Place the tongue in one cheek and push it out with a finger. Do the same in the other cheek.

Jonathan N. DePaz '96

An important part of the activity that the stroke has taken away from me was the physical exercises. I accepted the fact that I was not physically normal and able. However, I have to move on. The muscles—skeletal, smooth, and cardiac—make us do a whole range of movements such as, among other things, running, walking, laughing, breathing, smiling, and chewing.

Skeletal muscles are fibers which are long and cylindrical cells which bind muscles to the bones, called *tendons*. Usually, the fibers are similar to bundles of wire and are the same length as the muscle. The *smooth muscles,* however, are not linked to the bones. The fibers have only one nucleus and are shorter than the skeletal muscle cells. Like the smooth muscle cells, the *cardiac muscle* cells have one nucleus but numerous mitochondria, (microscopic filaments) which are long and thin cells. They produce energy in the cells and are involved in protein synthesis and lipid (fat) metabolism. In a knee joint, there are bones such as: *ligaments* which connect bone to bone, *tendons* from bone to muscles, and *cartilage,* which acts as a cushion between bones.

Physical exercises are significant to a healthy body. The regular muscular activity strengthens the heart, enlarges the capacity of the lungs, and builds energy. The blood vessel in well-developed muscles gets its nutrients from the bloodstream. The exercises help me increase my strength, endurance, and flexibility. The purpose in mobilizing the muscles is to save the right extremities from being atrophied, which decreases the size of tissues.

Each joint has a lubricating fluid known as *synovial,* which provides free movements in the shoulder, elbow, knee, hip, wrist, ankle, and foot. The fluid protects the area from friction and enables the joints to bend, twist, or extend, allowing to use the full range of motion. Having much significance, the movement of the joints is vital. Normally, the synovial fluid greases the joints frequently. However, when the joint does not move, and the fluid does not lubricate the joint enough, it tends to dry.

The cracking of the joints is a sign that the fluid is deficient but, any kind of movement stimulates synovial fluids.

I bought a restorator, a clinical machine similar to a stationary bicycle that could be attached to my wheelchair. The first time I exercised, my paralyzed right leg was out of control. It was flapping right and left helplessly. It was apparent that only the left leg was pedaling the machine. I had to use my mind. My paralyzed right leg had to concentrate on pedaling and carry the body weight by itself. It was extremely difficult to do so. But, I was determined to keep it in a straight motion. To stimulate my paralyzed leg, I used the stationary bicycle every other day for an hour.

The gluteal (buttocks) muscles are used to walk on two legs while the quadriceps (thighs) assist in the extremity movement. The lower leg muscles connect the heel by the Achilles tendon. In the foot are small muscles that help in flexing, extending and moving the toes.

For the arms, I purchased a mechanical equipment stimulator. The instrument is a rolling stick about twenty-four (24) inches long by one inch diameter. Both hands hold the stick and raise it slowly in front of the body. My paralyzed right arm is extremely heavy but, the left hand forces to raise it on an even level. I move it, up and down. I do the repetitions ten (10) times. Then, I switch the stick to the back side of the body and do the same number of repetitions. The exercises are simple but, laborious.

Another helpful equipment is a stepper. It is similar to a staircase exercise—stepping up and down by switching the legs. It is a good exercise to loosen the knee, calf, and the lower limb.

Note: The following sketches depict my right arm with an imaginary aid.

ON-LAND EXERCISES

After some time, I started doing physical fitness exercises without equipments. I have to feel, look, and work good, although it cannot be achieved overnight. But I have the patience and perseverance to meet my physical endeavor. The movements need to bring all efforts to bear on one thing—to loosen a series of joints.

Arm: Lie down, concentrate on the right arm, stretch it and raise it in front from the shoulder to the elbow, and to the wrist. Do small circles fifteen (15) times clockwise and fifteen (15) times counterclockwise. Do the same to the left arm.

Leg: 1. Lie down, legs straight. Lift the right leg at least six (6) inches off the surface, point toe and flex, alternately. Count twelve (12) times. Do the same on the left leg.

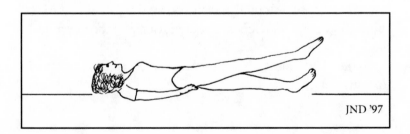

2. Lie down on the left side of the body. Lift the right leg about twenty (20) inches off the surface. Lower the leg without touching the surface and do twelve (12) repetitions. Turn the other side. Do the same with the left leg.

JND '97

3. Lie down with both legs straight on the surface. Slowly pull the right knee to the chest. Hold for ten (10) seconds and relax. Repeat on the left knee.

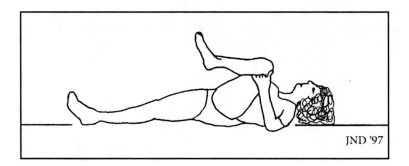

JND '97

Stomach: Lie down, bend both knees and keep both feet flat on the surface. Weave the fingers behind the head, close to the ears. Pull the head forward gently by the power of the stomach. Hold for five (5) seconds and relax. Repeat six (6) times.

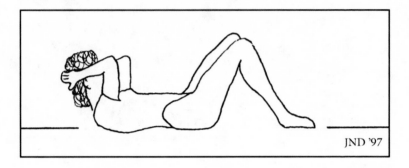

Pelvic: 1. Lie down, bend the knees with the feet flat on the surface. Raise the buttocks slowly until an imaginary thirty (30) degree-line is straight. Hold, tighten, and lower the pelvis back to the surface. Repeat on the count of ten (10).

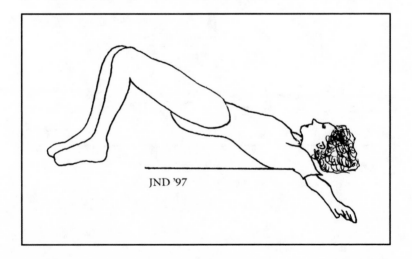

2. Lie down, bend the knees with the feet flat on the surface and flex the hips. Press the lower back slowly to the surface. Hold and relax. Repeat three (3) times.

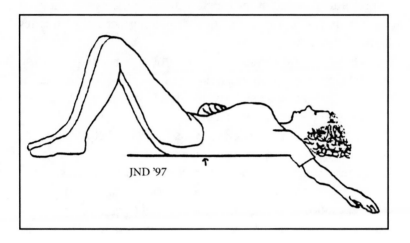

JND '97

AQUATIC EXERCISES

Essential to the development of disabled muscles are the aquatic exercises. They develop coordination, strength, endurance, flexibility, and agility, in isokinetic exercises which contract the muscles in an even amount of tension at a constant speed over the full range of motion. The tone or muscle endurance is achieved against the water's resistance. Aquatic exercises are a total mind and body water work-out, just like the land exercises. However, because the water provides resistance, it is more difficult to move, especially walk, in the water than on land.

The swimming pool water temperature is warm, between 84 to 94 degrees Fahrenheit. It is best to do the range-of-motion exercises at the higher end temperature while aerobic exercises should be done only at the lower end temperature, to prevent overheating.

Because aquatic therapy provides increased muscle resistance, it lessens the pain and fatigue. Immersing the body in water to the shoulder level while exercising, the joints and muscles are relieved of the pressure and stress caused by normal land activity. At the same time, it strengthens the muscles around the joints.

One of the important features of the swimming pool is the handicapped ramp with rails, sloping from the pool entrance to the pool water. Because my paralyzed half-body could not handle my body weight, I could not use the ramp. My leg buckled down when I tried to pace. With the help of two (2) swimming pool lifeguards, they lifted me from the wheelchair to the pool deck, then slowly dropped me to the therapist in the water, who carried me to the pool work-out location. I held onto the pool wall but my paralyzed right leg was floating. I could not stay firm. A two-and-a-half pound (2-1/2) weight was placed on my leg. But my leg was too buoyant that another two and a half pound (2-1/2) weight was needed. To get me out of the pool, the therapist, with help from the swimming pool lifeguards, lifted me from the water and sat me onto the pool deck. They then carried me back to my wheelchair.

After seven (7) months of working out in the pool, my legs and my body balanced out. It was quite an experience to walk in the parking lot without holding on to someone, especially since the field is a huge open space. With some sensations in my paralyzed leg, I walk with proprioception—an awareness of the way I move with the knowledge of my position, weight and resistance of objects in relation to my body. I learned to walk through the pool ramp to get to the water. The years of endeavor are paying off. I can walk a distance of one-hundred fifty (150) feet without resting.

Water has a curative power on my body. My disabled leg is improving faster than I expect. My right foot did not sit flat, always on its edge. My ankle was twisted and my leg was bowed. Under no certain terms can I stand without a foot-leg brace. However, through battling water-resistance, my ankle and bowed leg are now nearly straight. I can walk in the water without holding onto the pool wall. It is a milestone. I came a long way but I still have a great amount to achieve. I believe that by continuous water therapy, I will meet my goal.

There is a relation between staying healthy and keeping clean. The relation is germs. The human body has numerous microscopic parasites living on the human skin. They live within, upon, or at the expense of another organism whose body obtains nutriments. They are nourished and strengthened with the sustenance of dirt which breeds germs. There are harmless and harmful germs. Certain bacteria and viruses are harmful and they intrude upon the body. The skin is a barrier to prevent germs from entering the body and causing infection. A warm shower, with soap, is a killer of germs and cleanliness is the main defense against the hostile parasites.

Part of my hygiene is clipping nails of my hands and feet. Having only the left extremity working, it is easy to nail clip the right extremity. But when it comes to clipping my left finger nails, I attach the clipper to a stool bench and use my left foot to click the clipper as it clips the nails of my left fingers. Hygiene maintains a hopeful and great self-worth attitude which gives me a positive approach to life.

Full-Range of Motion: Stand straight in shoulder-deep water
with back against the pool wall. Raise one leg, swinging it
to the right and left on the count of fifteen (15).

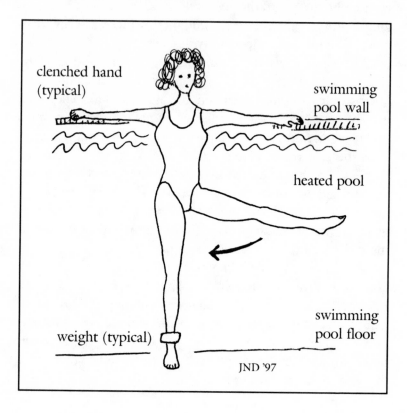

Arm: Stand straight in shoulder-deep water. Hold both hands together with the palms down. Press the arms down and push up with the same force. Count to ten (10).

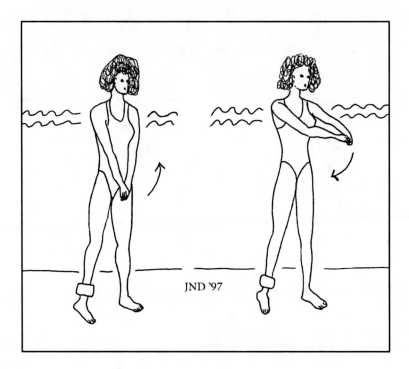

JND '97

Ankle: Stand straight in shoulder-deep water with the back
    against the wall. Raise one leg and, keeping it straight,
    rotate the foot by the ankle in a clockwise circular motion.
    Do it for ten (10) seconds. Repeat in a counterclockwise
    motion for ten (10) seconds. Then, switch to the other leg
    for the same length of time. Do the same routine with flexed
    toes.

JND '97

Hips: Stand straight in shoulder-deep water. Raise one leg in
front to a 45 degree location and rotate the foot about the
hip clockwise for ten (10) seconds. Repeat in the counterclockwise direction for the same length of time. Repeat the
sequence with the other foot.

JND '97

Legs: 1. Stand straight in shoulder-deep water. Hold on to the
pool wall, keep the leg straight, while swinging the leg from
front to back for ten (10) seconds. Reverse the position and
repeat the exercise on the other leg.

JND '97

2. Stand straight in shoulder-deep water, facing and holding onto the pool wall. Lift heel and then relax. Repeat to the count of ten (10).

JND '97

Upper Leg: Stand straight sideways in shoulder-deep water.
  With both feet flat on the pool floor, hold on to the wall.
  Kick heel up while bending from the knee only and hold for
  ten (10) seconds. Repeat on the other leg.

JND '97

Hamstring: Stand straight in shoulder-deep water, facing and holding onto the pool wall. Bend front leg and straighten back leg. Hold for five (5) seconds. Relax. Do the same on the other leg. Repeat the sequence three (3) times.

JND '97

Shoulder: Stand straight in shoulder-deep water. Twist the upper body from left to right to the count of ten (10).

Shoulder/Neck: Stand straight in shoulder-deep water. Swing the arms straight, crossing front of the body, then straighten. Repeat to the count of ten (10).

Shoulder/Chest: Stand straight in shoulder-deep water. With hands on hips, pull shoulders back and bring chest forward, then reverse and bring shoulders forward while hunching back. Repeat to the count of three (3).

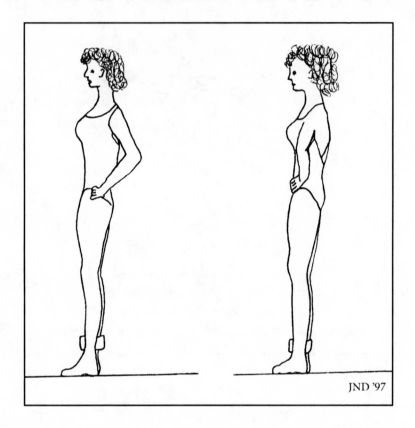

JND '97

5

LOOKING BACK

I HAVE TO RECOUNT MY PERSONAL LIFE. I conceived that stress has an impact on my well-being.

Once upon a time, I was born in the Philippine Islands, islands in the Pacific where the sun was torrid and the day was long. In the archipelago, life is simple and easy. As the breeze whizzes by, it brings in the two seasons of the year—the dry and the wet seasons. Drought is common in the islands during the dry season when it is hot, humid, and sweltering with burning bright sun. From June to September, monsoon occurs—the seasonal wind of the Indian Ocean and southern Asia. Monsoon is extraordinary, mysterious, and enigmatic. Sometimes the cloud bursts and it rains heavily for ten (10) consecutive days. With the strong monsoon wind and torrential rain, the wet season is so powerful that the water overflows and the town floods.

Many years ago, my father was a county deputy sheriff and my mother was a business woman with a convenience store. Mother was a pretty woman—the belle of the town of her birth. She was white-complexioned with Spanish features. Dad was dark and honorably handsome. He came from a good, aristocratic family. He was outgoing and he loved to live life to the fullest. His coconut plantation and his regular job with the government supported a family of six children. I have four (4) sisters and a brother: Pat, Marieta, Myrna, Gilda, and Hector.

75

I was raised in a Roman Catholic environment, where a majority of people practiced Catholicism as part of their culture. Sunday, the first day of the week, is Sabbath, a day of worshipping. In every sector of government or private affairs, it is the norm to observe every holy day of obligation. I feel that the religious practices are routine, stereotypical, and the belief system has been spoon-fed. Questions showing religious doubts are not and cannot be tolerated. Because of my inquiring mind, I have to understand basic questions about life existence. That made me different.

My family are church-goers but I am not. I am a lapsed Catholic who explores life freely. I feel I communicate with God explicitly the way I do. There is no question about my belief in God. My wholehearted love for and faith in Him are unconditional. I talk to Him regularly in gratitude and account of daily happenings. He is my Savior. He is always there for me. I believe that whatever happens, He means it for a reason.

My dad came into my life, when I was four (4) years old. He was in the military during World War II. He was a strict man but he taught me how to write. All the while, he was holding his belt ready to spank me as soon as I made a mistake. But I was a good kid. The belt hit me only once the whole time I was learning to write. After a month, he disappeared, and reappeared a year later. I started grammar school when I was five (5), which was the norm as soon as a child learned to read and write. I was quiet, but observant.

When Dad was away, he sent me letters, in an unusual way. He gave me a pet name, Delly. I started school but I could not understand most of the things he mentioned in the letters. He never wrote Mother although the letters were clearly meant for her. I did not know what was going on. Young as I was, I could feel Mother's disgust. It went on for a long time. It built the repulsion deep inside her. At times, I did not understand why she spanked me for no reason at all.

One day when my sisters were home playing with dolls, I decided to go out in the backyard. I climbed trees and played with the pigs by swishing a tree branch. I got carried away by the reactions of the pigs that I fell into the large pigs' sty. It was muddy black and smelly. I yelled for help. Pat came. She dropped a long stick and told me to hold on to it as she pulled it. She saved me from drowning from the black mud. I went into the house. Mother was furious; she gave me a good spanking. Apparently, I did something wrong.

I vividly remember an event that seems to contradict scientific laws during one of the wet seasons of the year. I was about six (6) years old when Mother sent me and Marieta to town to have our hair permed. Because the beauty parlor had a tight schedule, we had to have it done that day. We took a shortcut to the business district by going through the river side-street. It was not raining but little did we know the river embankment eroded and the river overflowed.

We started wading but, to our surprise, the water was deeper than we expected. Nobody was around to help us get out of the wade. All of a sudden the wind pushed us to a deeper area. I was alarmed by the water depth being erratic. The waves were strong and when I turned around, Marieta was far away. She was yelling between bobbing in and out of the water. Marieta was four and a half years old, tiny and shorter than me. It worried me because the waterline was up to my neck. I was scared we did not know how to swim. There was nothing to hold onto and the waves were not letting up. I could not turn around easily because I was fighting the wind. I was afraid to fall into a deep zone. We could not hear each other anymore so, with a clarion voice, I yelled and said, "Keep praying. Only God can save us." The next thing I knew, we were at the edge of the water. We just walked out of it. To this day, I cannot believe it. An angel must have carried us to dry land.

Since my dad was always away, my grandfather and uncle visited us a few times. When I was born, Uncle Mac concocted a name from my parents' names. The first syllable, "Ma" was from "Marciana" and the last three syllables "delina" was from "Fidelino." Because of gender, the last letter "o" was changed to "a."

After my grandfather talked Mother into moving out to Dad's town, which was a day's travel, she finally gave in. For the first time, there was a man in the house. I was eight (8), aloof, and remote. I saw Grandpa often. His house was more than a mile away from ours. But in the early mornings of dawn, on his way to the farm, he made it a point to stop by our house to give me a hug and a kiss while I was sleeping. He was an easy-going, caring and loving man. At a young age, I felt loved and cared for.

Every weekend, I stayed with Grandpa and Grandma in their big house. Grandpa was a carpenter, handy-man and a friend to everybody. Grandma was an aristocrat, bejeweled, and dressed-up with gowns made of silk, *jusi* or cotton. She owned rice and coconut plantations. Every day she walked to the market with her maid holding the parasol to protect her from the sun while Grandpa took care of the farm.

Grandma always had something for me—a good *merienda* and pieces of jewelry, such as a 14-carat gold necklace, pearl or garnet earrings and rings. Every Sunday was feast day. Each meal was a dinner with many different entrees. Grandpa made sure that I had my favorite dishes. Because I grew up skinny, my folks thought I was not eating enough. Grandpa used to say there was no reason to be hungry.

He loved carrying me in his arms and showing me around. He would take me to their second house, a stone's throw away from the big house. The second house was beautifully built on a high terrain where the steps were made of boulders. The back yard was a mile of forest and the front yard was landscaped with different fruit-bearing trees. By the front bedroom window, he used to put me on his shoulders so I could pick exotic fruits from the tree. I cherish that moment. Easily, I became a part of his life. Until one day, he was gone.

For days, my dad, his brother and friends searched for Grandpa. They found him floating in the river. Somebody murdered Grandpa and threw him in the river. It was horrific. Why would anyone kill a man without a wicked bone in his body? I heard that politics had something to do with it. I felt crippled and abandoned by his death. It stirred my world and grief devastated me. Every mile I tread, I think of him.

My life went on with despair. As years went by, my relationship with Mother worsened. I had to be out of her sight. Since I did not play with dolls, I chose the trees as my respite. I climbed trees, relaxed on the branches, and pondered about life. I realized that if Dad would not show up for days, she would turn to me as her outlet of grudge. She could see my dad's image in me that reminded her of his absence. It was simple to read her feelings. I became the vent of her unhappiness. When Dad was gone, she was cranky. And whenever he was home, she was jubilant.

One afternoon, I overheard my parents talking about me. Dad asked Mother why she never bought me anything, especially that day when I needed a new pen for school. Her reply was, "She does not need it." He felt it was unfair to cross me out. The next day, Dad told my aunt about it and it only took Aunt Miniang a heartbeat to get me what I needed. My aunts and cousins bought most of my stuff for school. From time to time, they gave me pocket money. That was how good they were to me.

One day, Dad and his friend went out to see a movie. It was about a family who had several children. One of the daughters was mistreated by the mother. She laid off the maids and made her disfavored daughter the family servant. The mother disliked her daughter because she was dark-complexioned. In the islands, being dark is ugly, so to speak. When Dad came home, he told us the movie he saw and he asked us to listen to the story. At the end of the story-telling, he said to Mother and my siblings, "I think of Delly when I was watching this movie. I know she is being mistreated in the same way as the girl in the movie."

The mother in the movie was the spitting image of Mother.

I lived a normal life, in the realm of reality, and fixed my attention to my schoolwork. I was active, popular, an honor student, and a student council member. Some of the extracurricular activities in school were public speaking, declamation, and oratorical contests. One of the classrooms had a stage where we learned how to talk in front of the audience, without the use of a microphone—be it a school political campaign or debating contest. I was at ease in public speaking and oration. Once a year, the school had a convocation where each high school year presented the cream of the crop. They had a program consisting of speeches, classical music, and drama.

One school day, the school principal informed me that I was in the convocation program. He wanted my dad, being well-known for his eloquence in speech, to write the oratorical piece that I would deliver. I told him I was not sure of that because my dad did not want to be involved with school affairs. When I was getting help for school homework, Dad used to tell me that assignments were for children and not for parents. Because of that, I told the principal that I would talk to my dad about it. I had time to ponder because Dad would not be home for a few days.

My dad was the provincial warden and he lived in the provincial capital residence. Every time he was home, he would check my schoolwork and asked me how I was doing. I told him everything was fine although I had one problem. The principal wanted him (Dad) to write an oratorical piece for me to be delivered on the coming school convocation program. He asked me a few questions and finally committed himself to do the oratorical piece. He coached me on how to stand, memorize, look and speak to an audience as well as when to be forceful in some parts of the speech. He took some time off to watch my final oration. He was pleased, although I did goof once.

A couple of years later, the townspeople requested my dad to enter the political arena to beat the incumbent mayor. The mayor had not done anything for the people and its town. Dad was not, even once, employed in the town, but he was aware of what it needed. He thought about it, considered the ramifications and then accepted the challenge. His political party was independent.

Our family life changed drastically. I experienced waking up in the early mornings with a lot of unknown people having breakfast in our house. The house was big, holding about fifty (50) people for dinner. Every day was an open house with at least five (5) maids doing various work like house cleaning, laundry, grocery shopping, cooking and running errands.

In spite of the fact that Dad was extremely busy, he made sure that we were taken care of. We had bodyguards to stay with us all the time. At night, we had several soldiers guarding our house and its vicinity by hiding in the bushes with their guns, ready to fire. My dad received several threats on his life. It was tough to be in politics; security guards were indispensable. I was about fourteen (14) years old when I saw what it meant to be a mayoral candidate.

I resolved to help Dad. I talked to one of our bodyguards about my plan and he went for it. I asked him to hide it from Dad; otherwise, he would abort it. The town had thirteen (13) districts along with its contiguous rural territory. With Marieta and a few bodyguards, I went out to some remote districts where I did grass-roots campaigning. It was a campaign from house to house that spanned several miles while our driver followed us in a jeep. We ended the journey as the moon started shining through. I was pleased. Dad won by an overwhelming victory—a landslide!

Pat graduated from high school and moved to the city. She enrolled in architecture and stayed in a boarding house for a year until my parents decided to transfer all of us to the same university, where all levels of education were offered—from grammar school to college. The private catholic university has an uncompromising education. Three of us, Pat, myself, and Marieta, enrolled in architecture, engineering, and medicine, respectively. Myrna was in high school, and Gilda, in grammar school.

We had a good time. Some weekends, we played various games, one of them being very similar to Ouija. A glass was turned upside down and rested on a board marked with words and letters used to spell out messages in spiritualistic communication. We turned off all the lights in place of a lighted candle. Someone was assigned to whisper greetings in a glass. Then, everyone would put a finger gently on top of the glass, without touching it, as the question was asked. Quietly, we watched where the glass was going. That moment, the spirit was answering Marieta's question, which was, "Will I meet the man of my dreams?"

The spirit in the glass answered, "Yes."

She asked back, "What is his name and where is he from?"

The spirit replied, "Noel Ferns, from the U.S Navy." We were thrilled that a name was mentioned by the spirit in the glass.

While we moved to the city, Dad stayed in the country where he was mayor of our town. He came to the city, most weekends, to touch base with us. Mother looked forward to the weekends when Dad would take her out to dinner and a movie or an off-Broadway play. She had wonderful times and Dad knew how to treat her. She was in heaven every time he spent time with her. But he made it a point to share some of his time with his children. He would stay with each one of us and check our schoolwork and class standings. It was a question and answer type of thing for my sisters before they ran upstairs to relax. I was distinct.

I stayed with Dad for the longest time. We would talk about current events, issues of the day and whatever I thought of. We had discussions about certain issues he was interested in. We debated often, and he learned to know my beliefs and find out my feelings about anything. That was when he realized I had a strength that would carry me through. I received pleasure in talking to him, albeit none of my sisters felt the same way.

To them, he was an extremely strict parent. To Dad, our decorum should be perfect and our manners impeccable. We had to be sharp because we had to know what we were talking about. It was either right or wrong, black or white and debatable or not. I had no problem with that. I saw it as a training to enter the outside world. As long as I was not doing anything wrong, I could not be bothered. My sisters could not believe that I was arguing with him. There were even a few times when Dad could not win a point over me and he would threaten to spank me.

Two months before I turned sixteen (16), I went to school at the college of engineering. It was a difficult time for me not educationally, but emotionally. I enjoyed the intellectual discussions with Dad and the time he spent with me. However, Mother was not happy. Because of her jealousy and insecurity, I seemed to be a threat to her.

Dad instructed me to stay with his sister, Aunt Ninang, every weekend. She was a school teacher. I helped her check school test papers, homework, etc. She told me that Dad had asked her to adopt me because he did not like the way Mother was treating me. But she told Dad she did not want to separate me from my sisters. She suggested that I come over on weekends and holidays to stay away from Mother. While their house was about thirty (30) miles away from mine, I grew up as Ninang's weekend daughter.

My school courses were held from afternoon to evening. A couple of guys in my class, Dodo and Gil, became my best friends. The platonic relationship lasted a long, long time until distance and time came between us. After our evening classes, they would walk me home until I was safe. They were like brothers to me. As close as we were, none of them knew my predicament with Mother. My sisters and I had different schedules. Mine was the latest. I slept late and got up late.

One morning I woke up early to study for school. I went downstairs to have breakfast in the dining room before I got to my work. I noticed the dining table was set and the food was covered. I peeked inside the plate and suddenly, someone hit my hand. I did not realize that Mother was behind me and said, "Don't touch that. Those are not yours."

I was stunned. There was no other food in the kitchen. The covered food on the table was steak, fried eggs, fried rice and a glass of milk. I was disgusted. I turned around and went back upstairs where I changed my clothes, picked up my books, and then left. It ruined my day.

I did not know what to do. The night before, I came home from school at about ten o'clock, and I had not eaten since. I was starving and I did not have much money. I was confused. I took a bus toward downtown but ended up nowhere. I landed in a church and sat in one of the pews to meditate, talk to God, and analyze my life. Should I quit school, leave home, look for a job? What would become of me? Was I one of her children? Or was I not? This happened a few times.

I stayed in church for five (5) hours, until it was time to go to school. I had an exceedingly bad day—no exclusive attention to my schoolwork. My school grades just got by. Regardless, I made up my mind to go on. It seemed Mother wanted me to peter out but I refused to give in.

In college, we had social activities. I was the class secretary and we planned a class party in a classmate's house. I knew I would have a problem with my parents about social life. Dad did not like us partying because our main concern should be schooling. My other sisters went to parties whenever Dad was not home. In my case, I could not play like that. I was not a social butterfly, but I had a social obligation to meet.

For a week, everyone was curious. But I knew Dad. Whenever he sensed that there was a party going on, he would try to catch the socialites. As the day was fast approaching, my sisters would keep asking me from time to time, "What are you going to do if he shows up?

My reply: "I have no choice but to go."

Saturday came and true enough, Dad arrived in the midst of the day. We greeted him and as usual, my sisters ran upstairs. He would talk to me while tying up my time. Since I was tight on schedule, I told him I had a party to go to. He pretended he did not hear what I said. I went upstairs and dressed up. As soon as my friend Dodo picked me up, I said good-bye and left. I knew Dad was not happy, but I had to do what I had to do. At the party, everything was running late, which meant I would be in deep trouble. The best thing I could do was be home by midnight. But I could not rush everybody. Dodo was worried for me and at about two (2) o'clock in the morning, he brought me home.

Half a mile away, we could see our house thoroughly lit. It was a sign that Dad did not sleep a wink and was waiting up for me. Dodo brought me home to my door and then left. I walked in, greeted Dad, and walked on through. He did not say anything until I was climbing the stairs. He said, with his loud voice, "Is this the time a good girl would come home, because I know that cheap girls do?"

I stopped, looked at him, and walked away without saying a word. I did not appreciate his remarks. He left the next day for the country. For weeks, I stayed quiet. I felt I did not deserve the bad treatment I was getting from him. A month later, I received a birthday card from Dad wishing me the best.

There was a medical student living two doors away from us who was going to the same medical school as Marieta. He was a school year ahead of her. I met him in the neighborhood and we talked briefly. Once he came over to our house to talk to Marieta about medical books and courses. One day, I ran into him in the neighborhood and he invited me to a dinner dance— his birthday party. I told him, I was not sure if I could make it. When the date was approaching, he came over to the house to ask Mother's permission to invite Pat, Marieta, and myself to celebrate his birthday.

The celebrant opened the dance floor by asking me to the first dance and the subsequent ones. It was easy to read his feelings. Unfortunately, Mother stopped by for a second and saw me dancing with the celebrant.

Mother talked to him and told him she had to take us home. She was furious for some reason. As soon as we got home, she pinched me and flogged me with a leather slipper. I yelled, "What did I do? Both of my sisters were dancing and you did not have a problem with that."

She called me names and she said I was flirting with the celebrant. The only thing I could think of was that she wanted the celebrant for Marieta. But I was not sure I wanted him for myself. Yet, all night long, the arguments and the beatings went on. In the islands, the parents are the gods. To be outspoken is unspeakable. Regrettably, I am. But I wanted to know what was going on.

I graduated from engineering school. A few months later, I landed a job by serendipity. I sent a "Letter to the Editor" of a major newspaper in the city, about a political issue involving my dad. Apparently, I impressed a business company president enough that he sent me a letter and offered me a job downtown. I checked it out, but it was not an engineering job.

To kill some time, I went to the Bureau of Coast and Geodetic Survey, a government firm, where my friend and colleague, Gil was employed. I met him and his girlfriend Chato, who became my best girlfriend. He introduced me to his boss and to the director of the Bureau. I talked to a few supervisors and before my visit was over, they offered me a job. I thought they were "putting me on" until they asked me to sign on the dotted line. I was ecstatic and the salary was very good for a new graduate. The following day, I started the job delineating maps and doing photogrammetry, making surveys and maps through the use of photographs. The maps represent the surface of the earth or the area of the sky.

In spite of the excitement, I had a problem. How was I going to tell Dad about my job? He told me before, I did not need a job and if I needed one, he would give me one. He had access to different governmental and private jobs. He had given jobs to other people, but I did not think he would give me one. When Dad came home, I talked to him by explaining the kind of engineering work I was doing and what I was being paid for. He was somber. He did not want to let me go and be independent. But I wanted to be autonomous.

A few years later, I moved to Erectors Incorporated, a private engineering firm fabricating structural steel, doing general construction and designing barges. It was there where I met Ted, one of the top three board certified architects in the islands and in later years, the first Illinois board-certified architect coming from the islands. Ted was intelligent and an unusually happy-go-lucky, hard-working architect. He had a liking in me, visiting me at home and meeting my family. It did not take too long to be close to him. I knew Mother sensed that. A few months later, Mother asked me if Ted were my boyfriend. I did not deny it. I told her that he was. She was furious, and she slapped me.

One day after work, Ted's best friend invited us to have dinner at their family house. The family wanted to meet me.

Unfortunately, the family members did not make it due to a serious traffic problem. At about eight (8) o'clock, Ted and I decided to leave and hailed a cab. I was not pleased with the way the evening concluded. However, the traffic slowed down a bit. As I looked through the cab window, my mind settled on a movie I saw a few days earlier. A young lady went home with her boyfriend who was not liked by her parents. Her mother was enraged; she hit her in front of her boyfriend and struck her repeatedly. He could not help her, so he left. That moment, the cab driver pulled into our residential lot and let us out. We came to the house and soon Ted left.

Living in the islands could not give me a feeling of satisfaction. I needed an uplifting power of achievement. The next day, I told Ted I planned to move out of the Philippine Islands—to migrate to the United States and use my profession as a stepping-stone to assimilate into American culture. He was afraid of letting me go. He knew I was certain of what I wanted to do. Without my knowledge, Ted went to the American Embassy and inquired about the possibilities of being an immigrant to the United States as a professional or even as a scholar. Ted was one of the architects of the Fulbright-Hayes Foundation for several years. As a professional architect, the United States Bureau of Immigration officer gave him the option of leaving the islands in three (3) months.

Two weeks later, Ted received U.S. approval. The embassy gave him three (3) months to migrate to the U.S. or he had to reapply. In less than three months, we were married in church.

Although I was married to a professional, I did not choose to come to America dependent upon one. I chose to migrate as a professional engineer. Because of this, I had to go through all the necessary requirements in order to be accepted as a professional. I had to pass psychological tests, medical exams, English language proficiency tests, and personal interviews. It was nerve-wracking. I was worried about how the examiners would rate me. In the final analysis, I was satisfied.

Six months before Ted and I left for the U.S., Marieta received her medical board certification in New York City after completing her medical internship. It was the turning point of her life. I thought I knew her. She was very private and secretive. She seldom wrote home. Unbeknownst to us, she had met a guy from the United States Navy, had a whirlwind romance, and then eloped.

We were preparing for my church wedding in Manila when Dad was overwhelmed by this discovery. He went to see the local parish priest in order to get my baptismal certificate which was required by the church in the city. The priest said, "I already sent her the certificate. She should have received it by now."

Dad replied, "Father, I think we are not talking about the same thing. My daughter is getting married and she needs a baptismal certificate."

The priest retorted, "Yes, we are talking about the same thing. She wrote me and enclosed a $30 check to send her a baptismal certificate."

Dad said, "But, my daughter just asked me to get it for her. I do not understand."

The priest replied, "Don't you have a daughter who is a doctor in New York City by the name of Marieta?"

Dad was shocked and said, "What? That cannot be true."

The priest said, "I am very sorry that you did not know about this."

Dad left the church and immediately came home. As soon as he arrived, I knew something was very wrong. He called all of us and told us the bad news. For days, he was writing Marieta, asking her to reconsider her plan. In the islands, it is a superstition for siblings to marry in the same year. Marieta eloped secretively in November and I got married in December. Had I known, I would have married in January the following year, which was not a long wait.

If Marieta wanted to come clean, she had to wait only three (3) weeks to end the year and to clear the old adage. She was a young doctor at twenty-two (22), so her biological clock was not a problem. She was just competing with her sisters, trying to be the first one to get married. All of Dad's begging was for naught. We could not do anything. After the wedding, I had to leave for the U.S. per the immigration's regulation.

At about the same time, we received a short letter that read, *"To Whom It May Concern: This is to inform you that your daughter Marieta and I got married. .... Jerry"*

What a shock! My parents were not "whom it may concern"! No man would write a letter like that to my parents. It was the height of irreverence to the max. Dad's hatred was beyond compare. I was worried; I felt sorry for Dad. How could Marieta forget the way she was brought up within the bounds of good moral conduct and behavior? How could she not know parental respect? How could she ignore the hard-working parents who sent her to medical school and granted her the best they could afford, ahead of the other children?

The day before Ted and I left for the U.S., Dad had a serious talk with me about Marieta's attitude and relationship with the family. He handed me a thick letter to be given to her. He told me the things that were in the letter. I was sad. He wanted Marieta to pay him back for all the money he spent in raising her and sending her to medical school. I told Dad my feelings about his request. Since he felt that he failed in her, he should just consider her a loss. He said he felt bad because he spent most of his money on her and he did not have enough for me. I told him not to worry, I had enough. Dad was upset. Marieta was so ungrateful she never wrote to explain what really happened. He felt the man Marieta married was not to be desired—the caliber of character and dignity were within reproach. I told Dad to give him a chance. I believed that he was worth something, even if he was not a doctor. Dad replied, "Slash the stone." Finally, Dad disowned her.

I found an engineering job in Chicago and a month later, Marieta came for a visit. I was excited to see her. In spite of that, I noticed her distinguishing character. She was flooding with condescension and denigration, on top of seeming all-knowing. I put it behind me and dealt with her with a purpose. I gave her the letter that Dad sent her. She looked at the envelope and tore it to pieces without any remorse. She did not even care to hear from Dad.

Five years later, I visited the islands to see Dad. I told him, "I plan to change my citizenship because the United States has the kind of life I have been looking for. I do not have a desire to come back to the islands. I will only come to visit you."

He replied, " I am hoping you will keep your birth citizenship but, if you think America is the place for you, I am giving you my blessing."

Marieta's husband, Jerry, went to the islands and looked for Pat in her downtown office. When he found her, he introduced himself and told her he wanted to meet the family. Although Pat explained the family's feelings towards him, she would see what she could do. Unexpectedly, Dad had a business meeting in the city, so he came into town. Pat got nervous. She talked to him and mentioned that Jerry was in town. Dad was indignant. He looked around and asked, "Where is he? I will gun him down." He thought he was hiding in the house. Pat replied, "He is not here, but he wants to come and meet everybody."

Dad was furious, he loaded his 0.45 caliber weapon and left. Late that night, Pat got so sick she had to be taken to the hospital. She had gastroenteritis, an inflammation of the stomach and the intestinal tract. Jerry visited her but soon after, Dad came. It was a nervy event and anyone there could read Dad's feeling. He stared at the man he had never seen before and one could sense a bad encounter ensuing. Pat felt Dad's intense dislike for the man. Trying to break the ice, she said, "Dad, this is Jerry."

Jerry extended his arm to shake hands but Dad refused the hand and left. Dad was caught off guard. He was not carrying his gun because he said, the hospital was not a place for violence. One thing about Dad was that he knew respect and consideration. He did not want to hurt Pat's feelings.

Dad might have mellowed through the years, but his animosity did not wane. His stand was strong and I never blamed him for that. Nevertheless, if Jerry ever promised anything, "the proof of the pudding is in the eating."

On July 3, 1982, Dad passed away. This saddened me deeply, for I had immortalized him even though I knew there would come a time when he would go beyond. But I was not ready to know how to live without him. His death was hard to accept, and I miss him terribly—his thoughts, his voice, his smile, his laughter, his countenance, and the fact that we used to write to each other.

With grief, I flew back to the islands. I could not sleep for days. I sat in his chair, from sunset to sunrise, hoping he would come and pay me a visit. I wore a black dress every day for a year. I still mourn and feel the chronic emptiness in my life. Nobody knew my dad the way I did. He left a thoughtfulness that would never die. He planted an exotic tree in the backyard of the house to commemorate the birth of my son, his first grandson. He passed away at 73. My brother Hector, who came later in life, was a good reflection of Dad.

The family made an arrangement to bury him in our city. However, the residents of the town where he officially served as mayor, requested my family to bury him in his hometown. They transported him to the country municipal hall where mourning people paid their last respects. The main street toward the cemetery was closed and the people walked a mile to join the funeral procession. With some dignitaries, he was buried in the town cemetery with the official gun salute.

Several years before he died, I bought a brand new house in a desirable neighborhood in Quezon City, Philippines. It has

My Dad

four (4) bedrooms, a living room, dining room, kitchen, toilet/ bathroom, terrace, front/back yards and maid's quarters with separate toilet and bath. The house was for my parents. Dad relished it. He lived with Mother and Hector but Mother refused to acknowledge my gift to them. After Dad passed away, I sold the house to my sister Myrna and her husband Cres so that Mother's life-style would not change. In addition, Cres and Myrna own another large house in Quezon City, where they reside with their four (4) children.

Years later, my dad's vault was unlocked, and certain treasures were unveiled: a scrapbook I made for him, my report cards from grade school through high school and college, my activity programs, and two letters I wrote. The scrapbook was my gift to him on one of his birthdays and I filled it with news items from major newspapers in the city about his political career.

Months later, after I came back to the U.S., I discovered I had a medical problem. My doctor concurred my findings—I had lumps on my left breast. Several tests were done and surgery was imminent. A day before the surgery, I dreamt of my dad. In this dream, I was dejected when suddenly Dad came and asked me, "Why do you look so sad? Do you have a problem?"

I answered, "Dad, I am going to the hospital for surgery. I have lumps on my left breast. I am scared."

Dad said, with a smile, "Don't worry. Do you remember when you were young, you used to hide from the doctor who was giving you shots? I laughed at you because I knew it was not painful. It's the same thing with breast surgery. It will not hurt you, believe me, the way an ant bites you."

The time came. The anaesthesia put me out and the surgery went well. The surgeon took out a couple of lumps in my left breast and the next thing I knew, I was in the hospital ward. The nurse gave me a prescription for pain-killers. During the doctor's visit, he asked me how the pain was. I told him I hung in there because I had a high threshold of pain. The truth was,

I did not feel any pain from the surgery. The long stitches were there but that was it. Fortunately, the lumps were benign. I felt my dad was looking over my shoulder all the while giving me courage and inspiration.

Gilda is the youngest daughter in the family. She was spoiled, got anything she wanted and could twirl anybody around her finger. When we were in school, our live-in maid used to walk to school with Gilda so that she could carry her books. We were apart—a disparity in culture, traits, and personality. I left the islands when she was about thirteen (13) years of age and she did not experience the life I had when I was growing up. Her advantage: she is Mother's pet.

After graduating from college, Gilda flew to the United States and stayed with me. At that time, Ted and I had a private retailing business in addition to our professional jobs. My sister-in-law Linda, handled *The Country Mart*, a pioneer in marketing Asian foods and gifts in Chicago, from Monday to Friday. Ted and I took over on weekends and holidays. The schedule worked out pretty well and the business was booming. When Gilda arrived, Linda shared the job with her until Linda decided to quit. For a couple of years Gilda stayed with me as a member of the family so her expenses were minimal. Nevertheless, Gilda was expensive. Oftentimes, she threw parties and other social activities in our home, that sometimes I wished there was a down social tone.

One day, Gilda decided to take a more promising job elsewhere so she got a store replacement. In a way, I was happy for her so that she would understand the various expenses that come with renting her own place. She had no problem with that and she found a studio apartment near downtown, not too far from my place.

Gilda talked to me about Mother's plan to come over from the islands as a U.S. immigrant. Gilda was having a problem because Marieta was not interested in petitioning Mother, despite her earning capacity. Either Marieta or I had to be the petitioner since we were both American citizens. I told Gilda I was willing to petition Mother. However, the pecuniary support was beyond me because of my family's financial concern. She said it was not a problem. She would take care of Mother's needs. So I agreed to petition Mother.

I was excited because I had been away from home for a long time. I was thinking that life would be better since Mother and I would be in a different atmosphere. I had a growing depth of understanding and could face the adversities in life. Let bygones be bygones. I was thrilled that for once I would have a mother. A parent as I am, my relationship with Mother cannot be that bad. I thought.

Mother's arrival came. Ted, Gilda, my son and I went to the airport to meet her. We were jubilant when she showed up. After the routine check by immigration, we headed home. Along the way, we greeted each other. The conversation went on with various news about relatives. I asked Mother, "How is Nanang Hilang?" I was referring to her sister.

She said, "I don't know. I guess, she's okay. They are so poor I cannot be bothered."

I could not believe what I was hearing. Mother was extremely cold, unfriendly and without feelings for her sister. She had no other siblings, yet she never liked Nanang Hilang who lived in the same town where Mother used to live. Mother did not want to deal with her and her family because they were indigent. It was the same reason why Mother never visited them. I asked Mother if she had sent her sister greeting cards on her birthday, Christmas Day, or other occasions. She said, "No, I am too busy." That hurts.

I had flashbacks to those cold and flat memories. It was natural for Mother to look down on people who were poor and ugly, per se. I had a hard time dealing with her. Nothing changed. As before, we argued and I kept everything in my mind. It was just like before. I felt uneasy around her, albeit I kept trying to make our relationship work. I knew she wanted a new pair of slippers. I went to a downtown store after work and got them for her. I stopped by Gilda's place and happily gave the slippers to Mother. She looked at them sneeringly and said, "I don't want that." She refused them fervidly. I had to take them back to the store.

Gilda lived in the other wing of our apartment building. At the time, my baby-sitter was not available to meet my son when the school bus dropped him off. So, I left instructions for my son to go to Gilda's place after school. As usual, my son called me at work to inform me that he was with Grandma. This gave me peace of mind.

After work, I went to Gilda's place to pick up my son but Mother said, "He is not here. Maybe he already went home."

I went home but my son was not there either. I went back to see Mother again and asked her if she spanked him. She avoided answering my question by responding, "I was mad at him because he was quite unruly while looking for paper he could write on. All of a sudden, he was gone."

I was worried, but my son would not run away.

Gilda arrived and I told her the problem. She went to the bedroom and she spotted something under the bed. She bent her knees to the floor and screamed. My son fell asleep under the bed, while hiding! I was relieved and we left. Later on, Gilda told me she talked to Mother because she had seen how Mother treated my son. Gilda said to her, "I can sense that when my sister is not here, you are transmitting your anger to her son. What did my sister do that was so bad you are mean to her? Tell me, is she your daughter or not?" Mother could not reply and cried.

It touched the chords of my mind. I wanted to understand the meaning of relationship, emotion, feeling, trust and love. What does a brother, a sister, or a parent mean? Is it not enough to be connected for all time by history and blood to feel the intensity of the union? I want to understand the significance of a profound bond that carries us together, beneath the layers of history. Shall we even maintain the civility of our relationship? With all the dolor I experienced in my life, I began to doubt the underpinning of my existence.

6

"EVERY CLOUD HAS A SILVER LINING"

ABOUT A COUPLE OF YEARS AFTER I WAS MARRIED, I became very ill. I was light-headed and nauseated. I left work and went to the hospital's emergency room. The internist suspected I had an ulcer. He gave me a comprehensive medical exam in the upper and lower gastrointestinal (G.I.) region including internal exam. But he did not find anything wrong with me, although I was ailing. I could not eat. Food made me sick. He sent me home to rest in bed. For days, my only activity was travelling between the bedroom and the bathroom, to throw up.

My condition worsened. I was throwing up green stuff, vile substances. That made me nervous. Once again, I was in the hospital. The internist gave me more tests but he still could not find anything wrong with me. Finally, he led my husband Ted, to the couch away from me to discuss my health condition. I guess I was not supposed to hear what he was telling Ted. The internist said, "Madelina believes that she is sick, but I cannot find anything wrong with her medically. I want her to see another doctor."

Ted asked, "What kind of doctor do you want her to see?"

He replied, "A physician who specializes in the study, treatment, and prevention of mental disorders. Here is the name and telephone number of the doctor I allude to."

When we got home, I told Ted I was not going to see any psychiatrist because I knew I was very sick inside, very sick. Most doctors have a self-fulfilling prophecy and if it does not turn out the way they expect, the patient is accused of being insane. I decided not to do anything but observed my condition. I took the pills prescribed and it put me to sleep twenty-four (24) hours a day. Ted was frightened. He was in tears because although I was not dead, he could not wake me up. He stayed home, kept me company and quit giving me the pills.

A day later, I felt better but I still could not eat. He took me out to feel the outdoor atmosphere, hoping I would have a desire to eat. I was recuperating from a disease that I did not know about. One day Ted noticed something.

He said, "I think you are pregnant!"

I responded, "What? That cannot be true. If so, any baby in my tummy will be dead by now, with all the internal tests that I went through."

He replied, "Your tummy used to be flat but now it has a little bulge and I know you have not been eating lately."

I got worried because of the different drugs I had taken. Suppose I was really pregnant? Will my child be deformed physically and mentally? I had my doubts because I had no warning signs of pregnancy. I did not miss a menstruation period and I did not have morning sickness.

A month later, I decided to call the internist who advised me to see a psychiatrist. After I introduced myself on the phone, he recognized me and said, "How are you? How's your condition?"

I replied, "Doctor, I have news for you. I think I know what is wrong with me."

He asked, "What is it?"

I replied, "I think, I am pregnant." The phone went silent for a while, a long while. Then it seemed to go dead. I continued, "Hello, hello! Doctor, are you still there?"

I was ready to hang the phone up when I heard his voice. Quietly the doctor said, "Yes, I am still here."

Then I said, "Aren't you going to congratulate me for being pregnant? And aren't you going to recommend an obstetrician?"

He replied, "Sure. But how do you know that you are pregnant?"

I answered, "Well, I'm just guessing, but think about it. You told me there was nothing wrong with me, right? And you know I don't get sick easily. Your tests even showed that everything was fine."

It was very evident that the news shocked him. He was aware that the medical tests administered and drugs given were quite dangerous.

I met an obstetrician with proper qualifications and after he examined me, he confirmed my pregnancy. I was four months pregnant. I talked to him about my medical experience before the pregnancy emerged. He became silent but gave me a boost by mentioning that in some cases the baby turned out fine. He did not give me any assurances, though. However, he said, "Sometimes, good things happen for a reason."

That was disturbing. A few days later, I was informed that the internist moved out to another state to practice his medical profession.

When I was eight-months pregnant, I was confined to the hospital. I was diagnosed as suffering from pre-eclampsia, a toxemia of pregnancy. It is a poisonous bacteria growing throughout the body in the focal area. This condition had to be treated properly to avoid the actual eclampsia, characterized by a coma and convulsive seizure. It is considered that one out of two hundred (1:200) pregnant women with pre-eclampsia develops eclampsia which, when not treated properly, becomes fatal.

Halfway through pregnancy, I put on thirty (30) pounds. The obstetrician's medical order was to lose a pound a day. A week later, I went into labor. The radiologist x-rayed my stomach and found out that my unborn child was a complete breech, whereby the fetal buttocks present rather than the head. Labor pain is unbearable, extremely agonizing. During the delivery, I was out most of the time. After eighteen (18) hours of torture, my baby boy came out wailing. I fell dormant and into a deep sleep. The nurses tried to wake me up, practically opening up my eyelids, but nothing helped.

For a week, I became very sick and turned yellow. During my fourth week in the hospital, the director came with the doctor in-charge of obstetrics and explained to me that my condition was unusual. I had liver complications which required me to stay for another two weeks. In the meantime, my child's umbilical cord and circumcision were healed. I had a better look at my son. I could not believe the wonder of God's human design. I was blessed with a bundle of joy—my gem.

I went home with my child but, once again, became very ill. I was losing weight fast from one-hundred ten (110) to ninety-five (95) pounds. Although I was bingeing on food, I would become weaker every day. I had serious insomnia, staying awake all night long while taking short naps during the day. The doctor diagnosed me as suffering from hyperthyroidism, a condition caused by excessive secretion of the thyroid glands, which increased the basal metabolic rate causing an increased demand for food. Immediately he confined me to the hospital and mobilized the staff. He was concerned about my weight and energy levels.

For two weeks I was a medical specimen of an anatomy gone wrong. I had visitors from medical schools study my condition. I was showered with arcane medical language, obscure medical codes, jargons, or medicalese. Using medicalese to and in front of non-medical patients is a deliberate elitism. It is a deception to withhold information from patients, communicating in a highly scientific region. It was a preview of what I would experience later on. Examples of major medical terms are: "cerebrovascular accident" meaning "stroke," "myocardial infarction" meaning "heart attack," "osteo" meaning "bone," "epidermis" meaning "skin," and "dermatitis" meaning "rash."

By mistake, I picked up information that I was scheduled for surgery the next day. It came upon me so unexpectedly that I became very distressed. But no one ever informed me. The body they were talking about was still mine and no one could take that away from me. Some doctors consider non-medical individuals to have minute intelligence whereby they cannot make rational decisions for themselves. Doctors feel that it is not worth explaining to them the complicated human machine. However, I have enough basic knowledge about my condition.

The surgical removal of a portion of the thyroid gland is an involving procedure. The size of the thyroid and its gland should be x-rayed before incision, to determine its exact location. If the portion of the gland being removed is not large enough, my condition will remain the same. However, if the portion of the gland being removed is too large, my condition will reverse to hypothyroidism, a condition due to the thyroid secretion deficiency. The outcome will be lower basal metabolism. They therefore scheduled surgery that I found to be insulting as well as unnecessary.

I tried to contact the internist but it was futile. It seemed as if he refused to talk to me and he left me a message instead, telling me that everything was fine. But it was not. And because of that, I packed up all my personal belongings and walked out of the hospital room. The nurse chased me as I walked toward the elevator and said, "You cannot leave the hospital just like that."

I replied, "Oh, yeah? Watch me."

Some, if not a majority of doctors, tend to show control, exercise power, and lack consideration of others. I can surmise that they are not willing to share medical information and decision-making. Their attitude is shown in different ways. It is like running a business—rush through the initial encounter, make quick diagnosis and standardized treatments, and leave the patients waiting, all of which will amount to their one goal—to profit from high patient volumes and surgeries. The medical profession business assists in the slow demise of the essential part of good medicine—the doctor-patient partnership consisting of understanding one another, discussing certain problem areas, listening to each one's concerns, and most importantly, working together as a team.

As soon as I got home, I called a friend, a pediatrician, Dr. Violeta Angara. I asked her if she knew an endocrinologist she could recommend. An endocrinologist is a physician who specialized in the science of the endocrine or ductless glands and their secretions, especially in relation to their processes or functions. She happened to know one, but the endocrinologist she had in mind was already preparing for retirement and was no longer accepting new patients. Nevertheless, she talked to him about my condition and he met me the next day.

The endocrinologist was an amiable gentleman. We talked and he was surprised to hear that the original internist had a perilous medical practice. He told me that his investigation revealed the internist putting me on antithyroid drugs four (4) times the normal dosage required, on top of the aborted thyroid gland surgery. The endocrinologist prescribed the same drug, *propylthiouracil*, with the right dosage and multivitamins for the nutrients I needed. He checked on me every week and monitored my weight. Months later, he retired and another internist, Dr. Coleman Seskind continued the thyroid treatment. After twelve (12) years of treatment, he gradually withdrew me from propylthiouracil. Since then, it has stayed in remission.

Later on, I suffered from chronic pyelonephritis, an inflammation of a kidney substance. I was given IVP (intravenous pyelography), a radiographic examination of the kidneys, ureter, and bladder after introducing a contrast medium. The onset is due to bacteria that enters the urethra, a duct for discharge of

urine from the bladder. When that happened, I became helpless. My right kidney became excruciatingly painful, and I
suffered a fever with severe body chills. I had to be taken to the
hospital's emergency unit immediately and given an IV push,
an application of antibiotic intravenously through prompt and
forcible injection. With an early enough detection, treatment
can be successful by avoiding alcoholic drinks, staying in bed,
and applying heat to the back area.

Part of my yearly medical examination is a Pap smear exam,
a test for malignancy based on the analysis of bodily secretions.
The test did not come out well and I was given another one for
confirmation. The tests proved to be conclusive. I had a mild
cervical dysplasia, an abnormal change in the tissues covering
the cervix uteri, the neck of the uterus. The surgeon performed
a cervical conization, an excision of a cone in the mucous
membrane of the cervix. It was later found to be benign.

Three days later, I was sent home from the hospital. But, I
hemorrhaged so badly that the blood oozed like a faucet. I
passed out. Ted called my physician. He was instructed to call
an ambulance to take me to the hospital's emergency unit where
the doctor would be waiting. When we reached the hospital, I
was frozen because I had lost a lot of blood. They had a hard
time finding an uncollapsed vein so that they could perform a
blood transfusion. The nurses poked my arms and legs in order
to hit the right vein and used a long needle as a lead to position
the blood in the vein. It was found out that the cervical stitches
had melted prematurely. In a few minutes, I was conscious.

My son was growing up faster than I realized. A baby-sitter
with a college degree in psychology helped me out. Ten months
later I went back to work while I planned my other maternal
responsibilities. Each night before I tucked my son into bed, we
talked—about anything. I did not read children's book or tell
him regular bedtime stories because I wanted to spend these
precious moments with him, teaching him what I had person-

ally experienced. I had been a working mother and felt guilty that I could not spend my days with him. However, he enjoyed our night sessions. It became our habit for many years.

We discussed why sometimes children had to be spanked or reprimanded despite the fact that their parents loved them. I told him there were days when children would misbehave so every now and then, parents would have to remind them how to act properly. For example, if he were told to go home directly from school and he ignored me, he would be spanked (or reprimanded) in order to remember the importance of that rule.

One day, this really happened. When his father and I dropped him off at school in the morning, I told him to go home by bus, directly from school because I did not want him caught in heavy afternoon traffic. He agreed to call me once he came home, but he never called. I called home, yet there was no answer. An hour passed by, and still no call. Being a latchkey kid, I became worried. I came home and found him there, fortuitously. He realized that he had forgotten what was asked of him because he stopped by his friend's house to exchange sport cards. He then said, "Mom, it was my fault that you worried over me. I am so sorry. Are you still going to spank me?"

I replied, "I have to. Otherwise, you will not remember what you are supposed to do."

Sadly, he said, "I guess, you are right."

He went to his room and lied down facing the floor, lowered his pants, and I spanked him on his buttocks with a bundle of rolled newspapers. He cried.

After a while, he was quiet. He then came out of his room and spoke as if nothing at all had happened. My son understood everything I taught him because my reasoning made sense. Sometimes, children need physical punishment to grow and improve in the right direction. "Spare the rod and you will spoil the child." He became disciplined, responsible, and independent—characteristics which would better prepare him to face the world.

His friends at Near North Montessori School and later, at The Latin School of Chicago, could not believe that he would tell his mother everything. They told him, "Don't tell your mom every little thing you do (re: sex, smoking, drinking, etc.). Mothers are strict, and you'll get in big trouble."

He replied, "You don't know my mom. She's great. And she understands. I can talk to her about anything. She will tell you if certain things are not good and she will advise you the proper way because parents know better."

Ted was a good father. They were always together until he was about nine (9) years old. My son is a smart, inquisitive child, especially in matters regarding sex. But his father could not deal with it. So, my son turned to me in order to be enlightened about life. We sat down and had long conversations. He asked me questions, some that were embarrassing to adults, but regardless, had to come to light.

He told me that he had heard a story about how we came to life. One of his friends told him that before he was born, God placed him in his mother's tummy. However, my son was confused because he learned that his friend's mother's tummy had grown without any incision. I looked at him and showed him a book about sex for kids, which I kept for nine (9) years. I gave it to him and asked him to read it first before asking me questions.

I told him parents knew more about sex than the children who had a limited knowledge on the subject. I left him for a few minutes. He was in awe and he yelled, "Mom! You mean, I was egg!"

I said, "That's right. Everyone of us came from the combination of an egg and sperm."

He felt proud that he knew more about sex than anybody else in his age group in school. I told him I would feel better if he would come to me for any questions, doubts, or concerns regarding sex. This drew us closer to each other, closer than ever before.

When he was five and a half years of age, his father took him to an ice skating rink in the city, just to introduce him to a new interesting sport. My son tried it and loved it. He told his father he wanted a skating coach to teach him more about skating. The coach gave him lessons and he practiced several times a week. That year, he won the annual beginner's skating competition.

He joined The United States Figure Skating Association (USFSA), the national governing body of figure skating and a member of the United States Olympic Committee. The quest for his ultimate goal started when he turned six (6). All of his summers were spent away from home. As soon as school closed, he would go to a six-day-a-week Harris Keon Hockey Camp in Canada for two weeks. He was a very good hockey player who was awarded The Most Improved Player trophy every year for the four (4) years he trained there. (Hockey became a part of his life, being a varsity hockey player in high school and a U.S. collegiate hockey player in college.)

Like clockwork, he spent part of the summer in Canada. The rest of the time was spent in Colorado Springs or California for figure skating, trained and coached by Barbara Roles-Williams. He came home just in time for the start of school during the fall. It was a hectic time-table but he loved being active. He did not experience summers in Chicago. It was difficult for me but we were connected by the telephone. We made a pact to talk every single day. The telephone became a part of our lives—we allowed "the fingers to do the walking." It was almost as if he were just in the next room and our distance from each other was not far at all. We talked about anything.

The fall season had different activities, more frenzied than the summer. My son went to The American Conservatory of

Music once a week for classical piano while he travelled with the All-Star Hockey Team twice a week. At the same time, he figure skated six days a week. I made it clear though that school work would always have to come first. During our long road trips to other parts of Illinois for his hockey games, he would finish school work in the back of our station wagon.

The Latin School of Chicago has an ample amount of homework for students but he never complained. He managed to complete his schoolwork and landed on the regular honor roll list. At a young age, he learned to be independent, responsible, and organized. He learned the importance of time management, juggling both his school work and skating activities successfully.

During his junior year in high school, he moved to Boston with a heavy heart to be with his new skating coaches, Evy and Mary Scotvold. This period of adjustment was formidable, but in order to pursue his skating career, he learned to cope with life's difficult trials. One certain test was when he injured himself skating, severely lacerating his left quadriceps by the heel of his right skating blade. This left him hospitalized and bedridden for three weeks. He could not walk without crutches until a physical therapist worked with him extensively.

Finally, he went back to his daily routine of rising at 5:30 in the morning to be at the ice rink skating at 6 A.M. He skated figures for the first forty-five (45) minutes. The rink was freezing and the air was arctic. The deafening silence was marred only by the crisp turns of blades cutting into the ice. This was followed by the free-skating session. Before hitting the ice, he jumped off-ice and stretched in order to warm up his body. Once he hit the ice, his adrenaline flowed and he came alive. He practiced all his jumps, spins, and competition programs. He did the moves over and over again until he was pleased with his performance. Then, he drove to The Rivers Country Day School, for several hours and went back to the rink for another three (3) hours of practice. The workout was routine for six (6) days a week.

As he entered manhood, his teenage years were fraught with normal problems—finding and adjusting his identity. He became short-tempered and in want of something in life that he could not pinpoint. That was when disputes happened. Understanding his feelings occurred when I received a letter from him which I show here in its entirety, including his underlined words.

Dear Mom,

I'm just writing to tell you I'm awfully sorry that I'm such a hard kid to put up with. But for some reason, I get hyper when my parents keep saying things over and over again. You must be thinking, "How should a parent act to their children?" I think you're doing a great job. Please hang in there with me. *I know I'm a pain in the ass, but I'm very grateful to have parents like you and Dad. Keep up the good work !!! I wouldn't be where I am without you. I'm just a loud, outspoken person (I guess) and so are you. Our feelings and thoughts clash, but what makes a great relationship is the willingness to work together and compromise. I'm sure raising kids has its own joyous occasions and moments. I'm saying it again, I'm sorry. I really love you (and Dad), and I'm ever so grateful for both of you. Please, just try to put up with me and don't back down from doing what you have been doing with me.*

Your loving (pain in the ass) son,

In retrospect, this letter reminded me of a time when he recaptured and depicted my quietudeness with his artistic ability at the tender age of seven (7) years old.

Year after year, he competed in different levels of figure skating and won the Upper Great Lakes and New England Regional Competitions, the Midwestern and Eastern Sectional

My son's sketch of me when he was seven years old.

Competitions, and reached the U.S. National Junior Figure Skating Championships several times. He took the highest level of skating—the Gold Figure and Freeskating Tests—and passed. Gold medalists represent the cream of the crop in figure skating, and this can be accomplished only through many years of dedication and hard work.

Unfortunately, he had an acute synovitis of the subtalar joint in the right foot. Synovitis is the inflammation of a synovial membrane which is the lubricating fluid of the joints. The injury was brought on by landing on his right foot while descending from vertical jumps. The pain was torturous in attempting midtarsal and subtalar joint mobilizations. Due to that condition, he received a bye from the U.S. Figure Skating Association, and automatically advanced to compete in the U.S. Men's National Figure Skating Championships. However, my son's skating career came to a halt. The time was not enough for his injury to heal, and he was unable to return to training at one-hundred (100) percent capacity. This was the turning point.

I made a serious decision. I met my son at a restaurant in Boston to discuss his skating career. He had a recurring physical injury that ruined his figure skating goal. I felt strongly that he should hang up his skates since he reached the pinnacle—the Gold Test. In place, I wanted him to concentrate on his college education. He understood my logic; however, it was difficult to accept. Skating was a part of his life. He perceived it as part of him, seemingly born with it and loving its many aspects. But, he realized the importance of the educational sphere and reluctantly closed the competitive figure skating chapter of his career.

He went on to Boston College, where he grew up exponentially while pursuing his college degree. He focused on schooling and it paid off. He was on the dean's list and earned academic scholarships. He participated in the Foreign Study Program and went to study at the University of Toulon, France. He relished living in France just as when he went to school at Le

Lycee Bertholet, in Annecy, France when he was in high school. He has the fluency of the French language because he started learning the language in grammar school. In junior year, he was awarded the Otto Alcaide Modern Language Prize for French.

He came home, graduated from Boston College, and worked at Northwestern Mutual Life. This all ended when he auditioned for Walt Disney's World On Ice "Aladdin." He started as the Aladdin understudy and in a few weeks, he got the leading role alternating with a second role. He travelled overseas and toured the United States doing the show.

After three (3) years, he quit touring the show and moved on to a more promising career. He presently teaches figure skating, hockey, and Tae-robics class in Southern California. In addition, he skates various professional ice and roller blade shows while shooting commercials, TV shows, and movie roles. Occasionally, he travels doing shows.

My son is my pride and joy. I cannot ask for more. His normal growth with strong will and intelligence show the fundamental sense of trust and dedication. He grew up emotionally balanced and without a sense of loss. There will never be a perfect human being. However, being what he is, he is nearly paramount to his achievements.

Part of my family here in the East Coast is a purebred young female Bengal Leopard Cat, born on January 13, 1993. Bengal cat is the result of a crossbreeding between a domestic feline and a wild Asian Leopard Cat. My furry friend, "Buffin," is affectionate and has traits of her own. She has breathtaking beauty with large oval green eyes and a wonderful glossy coat mixed with orange ground and sandy buff. Her spots are black on a light background. She is regal and she walks gracefully, like the "girl from Ipanema."

Even though Buffin has her own language, we communicate, nevertheless I discipline her and she listens while looking at me. I trained her successfully—not to go on top of the table, not to chew the carpet, not to destroy plants, not to rush me when I am fixing her meal, and not to ask for more food than I give her. I trained her to clean her plate first before asking for more food and to never touch my own food.

Buffin is independent. She does not bother me when I am working, although she may occasionally want my attention. One day, I decided to find out if she wanted to play. I bought her a toy—a fishing pole with a "bird" at the end of the line. Several times a day, I would say, "Buffin, if you want to play, give me the stick," meaning the pole. She would look at me and at the pole while I pointed it to her. After a week, she caught on. Whenever she wants to play, she bites the pole.

The game goes like this. While I am holding the pole and the line is lying on the floor, Buffin holds onto the "bird" and gambles by releasing it on and off. With the right timing, I pull the pole and she jumps high and low to chase the "bird." She gets so excited that she lets out a very funny sound. This makes me laugh, it is so hilarious! When she catches it, she puts it in her mouth so I cannot pull it out. That means, she wins. I am so proud of her I tell her she is good, she is great, and I love her. I can feel her exultation. In a proud moment, she is pleased with her accomplishment.

Buffin loves to play and stays awake during my waking hours. When the bedroom door is closed but left ajar, Buffin sits by the door. If I do not notice her, she makes a little noise until I invite her in. She responds when I call her and she understands the words: "c'mon," "wait," "just a minute," "finish it," "excuse me," and "look." Buffin is worth her weight in gold.

Recently, I adopted Sunny, a hybrid male kitten, a cross-breed between Russian Blue and Japanese Bobtail, born on May 19, 1999. His eyes are slanted almond-shaped and yellow. His shiny coat is blue and gray with an unusual pattern. His tail is unique—short and curly. The hairs of his tail grow outward in all directions which make them fluffy and bobby.

Sunny is playful and rambunctious. He taunts Buffin, who gets mad when he gets on the counter or he hides in the bookshelf after he pushes off its contents. Buffin is reserved and polite. She does not clutter the newspapers and magazines. Because Sunny knows he is tiny, only less than half the size of Buffin, he runs to me whenever he is in trouble. He hangs around me and peregrinates from my head to my lap. Sometimes he relaxes on my shoulders but naps on my lap until I wake him up. Sunny is very affectionate and loves hugs and kisses. He watches the Animal Planet shows on TV. Every now and then, he touches the TV screen and checks the TV top looking for the animal on TV. He enjoys drinking water from a mug (while I hold it) and eating ice cream with me.

The funny thing about Sunny is, he thinks the pet carrier is his bedroom. When he is tired and ready to retire for the night, he goes to the carrier and relaxes. That's when I turn off the light and say "Good night, Sunny, good night."

EPILOGUE

IN WRITING THIS BOOK, I accomplished a significant angle of my brain redevelopment. Since September 26, 1991, I have been fighting every phase of the stroke. One of the toughest things to beat is aphasia—the processing in the brain for the communication by speech and language. My brain is intact in the power of thinking, planning, and decision-making. However, it still presents problems with abstract elementary mathematical calculations. I am the same person inside and my memory is "cutting edge."

My recovery continues, without a doubt. My health condition, physical and mental, is in good shape. I do the land exercises daily and the aquatic exercises three (3) times a week. My paralyzed half-body has progressed to a semi-level; my face has become normally balanced; my right eye changed for the better although the blind spot is still there; my right ankle can control the twist to a certain degree; and my gait has improved. Even though my right leg is akin to a prosthesis due to the absence of feel, I trained myself to walk with proprioception.

Basically, I do almost everything practical except certain things that need, literally, a second hand. I cook, do my laundry, shop for groceries, run errands, and what-have-you. However, I cannot drive a vehicle due to my eye-impairment. I am still dealing with different unusual messages. My speech has improved tremendously but, I still cannot talk as fluently as I write. Words do not come out the way my brain transmits them.

Because of vast medical techniques and research, I am hopeful that in this lifetime I will see nerve transplants that will make the paralyzed extremities perform in a normal way. The improvements that I have achieved are tantamount to the region of possibility, while the road ahead is of great length. I survive the highs and lows of the storm as life flows through streams and valleys. But deep inside, there is no end, even in the life beyond.

In the midst of life's inevitable storm, I am filled with the blizzard of discontent and certain Herculean tasks. Nevertheless, barring unforeseen circumstances, my recovery is within the range of human endeavor. This book is a sign that I can beat the odds with my tenacity. I do not indulge in loneliness or allow decadence to win over me. I am determined to continue working in order to achieve my goal—to live normally with a hemiplegic body and even though I may be "sailing against the wind."

The disabled world is a stony uphill struggle, but my persistence to live goes on. Because of my living activities, I have come to realize that life is tougher than I expected it to be. Some able people are inconsiderate of aphasic survivors. I am disabled but I do not need to be handicapped. My disabilities are real, but so are my abilities. I hope this book will explain the physical and mental condition of stroke victims—that they are not mentally ill or idiotic prodigies. Their struggles come from the lost connection between brain and speech.

The medical diagnosis after I came out of the coma was simple: I was alive but I would be a living vegetable. I have proved that wrong. I believe that stroke is a challenge—to every survivor—and recovery is an attitude about life. What is past is gone, and I face a new beginning. I can never be what I was before, but I can build a new life. God gave me the strength to go on because He had a purpose in keeping me on earth. Each day is His gift to me, my gift to Him is how I spend each day. I am a futurist. I do not always follow the paradigm of life.

ACKNOWLEDGMENTS

Above all, I am grateful to God for showing me the will to write and bring this book into the world.

I am thankful:

To Lawrence & Memorial Hospital, New London, Connecticut; Bayview Health Care Center, Waterford, Connecticut; and Northeast Rehabilitation Hospital, Salem, New Hampshire—for allowing me to realize that there is a new world after stroke.

To the doctors, therapists, nurses, and assistant nurses—for their devotion to the disabled patients;

To Dr. William A. Colom and Dr. Daniel E. Moalli of Lawrence & Memorial Hospital, Dr. Charles A. Kessler and Dr. John T. Bowers, III, of Sentara Norfolk General Hospital, Dr. Kathleen P. McEntee, Dr. Alan F. Doyle, and Dr. Cynthia C. Su of Eastern Virginia Medical School, for my medical existence;

To Thomas A. Walther, for conservatorship of my estate;

To Jonathan N. DePaz, for editing and putting forth the illustrations;

To Paul M. Clemens, for publishing this book;

To Northside Pool and Therapeutic Recreation Center, for aquatic exercises;

To Orlando R. Cabanban and Cathy Maudlin, for photography;

And to Ming & Dave Almendral, Melanie Burke, Rick Maudlin, Cdr. John & Caroline Phillips, Pat & Magpayo Sayo, Mylene Sayo, Bea & Gene Sult, Lorraine & Roy Swintek, Mary Helen Thomas, Wili Tolentino, Clara Vallmer, and Angie & Mike Youngman, for touching my life and being there—the reason, at no time, I can be "an island."

BIBLIOGRAPHY

Ackerman, Sandra. *Discovering the Brain*, Institute of Medicine National Academy of Sciences, National Academy Press, Washington D.C.

American Heart Association. *The Family Guide to Stroke*, Times Books/Random House Inc, New York & Canada.

Asimov, Isaac. *The Brain*, Walker & Company, New York.

Bishop, Jerry E. "Stroke Patients Yield Clues to Brain's Ability to Create Language," *The Wall Street Journal*, October 12, 1993.

Cappasso, Tony. "Fat Treatment, New Drugs Can Cut Impairment from Strokes," *The Outlook Mail*, Copely News Service, Sept. 4, 1996.

Chant, Christopher. *Submarines of the 20th Century*, Tiger Books International, London.

Clancy, Tom. *Submarine, A Guided Tour Inside a Nuclear Warship*, Berkley Books, New York.

Edelson, Edward. *The Nervous System*, Chelsea House Publishers, New York & Philadelphia.

Elias, Marilyn. "Mood a Stroke Risk Factor," *USA Today*, April 16, 1997.

Flynn, John A. *Arthritis*, The Johns Hopkins White Paper 1998, Baltimore, MD.

Foreman, Judy. "New Technology Shows a Stroke in Progress," *The Boston Sunday Globe*, April 11, 1993.

Friend, Tim. "Drug Reduces Stroke Effects," *USA Today,* March 29, 1996.

Fincher, Jack. *The Brain - Mystery of Matter and Mind, The Human Body*, Torstar Books, New York & Toronto.

Hoeger, Werner WK. *Water the Aerobics Way*, Boise State University, Morton Publishing Company, Englewood, CO.

Joint Venture. Guide to Chicago Architecture - *AIA Guide to Chicago*, A Harvest Original, Harcourt Brace & Company, San Diego, New York & London.

Kaufman, Steve & Yogi. *Silent Chase, Submarines of the U.S. Navy,* Thomasson-Grant, Inc., 1989.

Kettelkamp, Larry. *The Human Brain*, Enslow Publishers Inc., Hillside, NJ.

Kolata, Gina. "New Brain Scanning Technique Can Show Stroke in Progress," *The New York Times,* Science Times, April 6, 1993.

Koop, C. Everett. *Stroke at a Time of Diagnosis*, Time-Life Medical, New York.

Margolis, Simeon. *Arthritis*, The Johns Hopkins White Paper 1998, Baltimore, MD.

Monmaney, Terence. "Trial Balloon," *Los Angeles Times,* Dec. 7, 1995; "Cerebellum Plays More Complex Role, Study Says," *Los Angeles Times,* April 26, 1996.

Ornstein, Robert. *The Amazing Brain*, Houghton Mifflin Company, Boston, 1984.

Parker, Steve. *The Brain and Nervous System*, Franklin Watts, London, New York, Toronto & Sydney.

Pedigree Books. *The Brain*, GP Putnam's Sons, New York.

Restak, Richard, M.D. *The Brain*, Bantam Books, Toronto, New York, London, Sydney, Auckland.

Rodengen, Jeffrey L. *The Legend of Electric Boat,* Write Stuff Syndicate, Inc., Ft. Lauderdale, FL.

Siino, Denise Marie. "Chamber of Hope," *Los Angeles Times,* May 22, 1996.

Snyder, Solomon H., M.D. *Brain Function*, Chelsea House Publishers, New York, New Haven & Philadelphia.

Sova, Ruth. *Water Fitness After 40*, Human Kinetics, Champaign, IL.

Spitzer, Terry Ann. *Water the Aerobics Way*, Boise State University, Morton Publishing Company, Englewood, CO.

Thompson, Richard F. *The Amazing Brain*, Houghton Mifflin Company, Boston, 1984.

Ubell, Earl. "New Victories," *Parade Magazine,* November 6, 1994

ABOUT THE AUTHOR

MADELINA AGAWIN DEPAZ worked as a nuclear engineer for General Dynamics Corporation after schooling, training, and certification. She received a Bachelor of Science in Civil Engineering degree from the University of Santo Tomas, Manila and a Master of Science degree from Rensselaer Polytechnic Institute, Troy, New York. Recently, Ms. DePaz received her Master of Business Administration degree from Rensselaer Polytechnic Institute, Hartford, Connecticut. She currently lives in southern California with her furry friends, "Buffin" and "Sunny."

Printed in the United States
114634LV00001B/346/A